Runner's Training Journal

By John Stanton
Founder of the Running Room

Personal Information

As the information in this journal is vital to its owner, please return if found.

Name:_____

Address:_____

City:_____ Postal/Zip:_____

Telephone:_____

E-mail address:_____

Running Gear Information

Shoes:_____ Size:_____

T-shirt:_____ Size:_____

Training shirt:_____ Size:_____

Shorts:_____ Size:_____

Tights:_____ Size:_____

Gloves:_____

Hat, cap, toque:_____

Personal Records

Distance	Time	Race Name	Date
5 km			
10 km			
½ Marathon			
Marathon			

Publisher: Running Room Publishing Inc.

9750 – 47 Ave.
Edmonton, AB T6E 5P3
Canada

www.runningroom.com

Runner's Training Journal / by John Stanton.

Includes index.

ISBN 978-0-9739379-8-5

Cataloguing data available from Library and Archives Canada

Graphic Design: Harsh Deep Verma, Brenda Fortin, Jessica Gould, Donna Leo

Copy Editor: Kristi York

Acknowledgements

A training journal is different from a regular book, as you—the runner—write half of it. This journal is a place to monitor your training, as well as a private area to write down your running goals and aspirations. Adding entries to the training journal provides an escape from daily technology and instills a sense of empowerment and satisfaction as you record your life as an athlete.

Included in the book are basic reminders, training schedules, inspiring photos and motivating quotations. You must now supply the perspiration and commitment to see your goals through to fruition. A written account of your daily regimen provides you with a clear reflection of your training and allows you to visually track your progress.

I would like to acknowledge all the people and their talents at the Running Room. To copy editor Kristi York, graphic designers Brenda Fortin, Jessica Gould, Donna Leo, lead designer Harsh Deep Verma, and project leader Mike O'Dell, thank you for your shared passion and many talents. Team commitment and the desire to be the best delivered this training journal in its friendly and informative format.

Table of Contents

Introduction

Welcome to the Runner's Training Journal.

Running is both social and personal. Some days, a run is just for you, and it becomes a very individual and meaningful experience. Running with others might be for competition or simply for completion. Running on your own can help you achieve clarity and calmness, while a group run expands your circle of friends. The solo run works on your self-discipline and courage; the group run allows you to be childlike and think of your running as play.

By recording your training, you can go back over days, months and even years to see what worked or what didn't. You can chart out the duration and intensity of your training. You may look back at your notes about the routes you took, the weather conditions, and even your training buddies. More than anything, this handwritten journal is something you can hold, feel and read—an expression of your innermost goals and aspirations.

We designed this book as a training guide and as a personal diary of your running. In the initial chapters, you will find lots of helpful advice, including shoe selection, stretching exercises, and safety tips. The training schedules provide a tested and proven program for everyone from the beginner to the marathon runner. The diary has plenty of room to enter daily training information and 12 months of space to record your activity. Each week has a great summary graph to display your week at a glance.

Once you fill in this journal, it truly will become your book—authored by you, about you and your training. Your journal will become a very personal extension of your training program as you reflect on your training, make necessary adjustments, and set future goals. Away from technology, it gives you a view into the soul of your training. So have fun, train smart and enjoy writing your running story.

I look forward to seeing you on the trails and at the races!

Committed to fitness and health,

John Stanton

Building Your Program

Chapter 1

The Running Room Training Principles

Stress and Rest

Stress is another word that can be used for training. In brief amounts, exercise (or training stress) causes a temporary imbalance in the muscular and cardiovascular systems. In response to this imbalance, the body reacts by reestablishing equilibrium and becomes stronger, to protect itself from further imbalance. Over time, the amount of training stress must become greater to promote further training and growth.

Rest should always be combined with training stress, as repair and reaction to the imbalance can only happen when the body is at rest. The rest period should be long enough to allow almost complete recovery from the training session, but not so long that the training adaptation is lost. When the rest period is too short, or the stress is too great, the body doesn't have time to repair and adjust, which may cause possible fatigue or injury.

Implementing principles of stress and rest into your program will ensure an adequate training stimulus followed by an appropriate rest period. Even in the early stages of a fitness program, physiological balances can be reestablished in approximately 24 hours. Start out by exercising no more than every other day or a minimum of three times per week.

Practicing the principle of stress and rest will also ensure that the training stress is consistent. If a few days of training are missed, the body may lose some tone and endurance. A day or two of hard training will not make up for what was lost. In fact, it may hurt you in the end by causing undue fatigue or injury. Consistency of training is critical for success. The individual who trains consistently will see greater improvements than one who trains extremely hard at times and skips training at other times. Think of rest as an important part of every good training program.

Consistency also has its rewards. As proper training continues, an individual will develop a solid fitness base. A solid fitness base will ensure that when interruption to training does occur for a short time, loss of fitness will be minimal.

The stress and rest principle of training is the foundation of any training program. Its purpose is to ensure an appropriate amount of training stress and adequate rest periods, resulting in a consistent pattern of exercise.

Progressive Overload

Running seems to attract hardworking, goal-oriented people who appreciate the fact that the sport rewards honest effort. These individuals have learned that the more they put in, the more they will get out. Running is different. Your willpower and your heart-lung machinery can handle much more work than your musculoskeletal system. At a certain point, it's better to relax about your training than to approach every workout in overdrive. The following guidelines show you how you can safely enjoy your running without risking injury.

1. **Honestly evaluate your fitness level**

   If you haven't had a physical exam lately, have one before you begin your running program. Start out running gently and slow to a walk when you feel tired. Remember, you should be able to carry on a conversation as you run. If you're patient with yourself, you can increase your effort as your body builds strength and adapts to the stress of running.

2. **Take it easy**

   The generally accepted rule for increasing your distance is to edge upward no more than 10% per week. Beginner runners should add just 1 or 2 km per week to their totals. This doesn't sound like much, but it will help keep you healthy, and that means you can continue building your distance. Start from a base of 20 km per week; you can build up to 40 km per week (enough to finish a marathon, if that interests you) in 10 to 12 weeks. Your long runs are another consideration. To avoid injury or fatigue, these should be increased by only 2 km per week.

3. **Plan for plateaus**

   Don't increase your distance every week. Build to a comfortable level and then plateau there to let your body adjust. For example, you might build to 20 km per week and then stay at that training level for three or four weeks before gradually increasing again. Another smart tactic is to scale back periodically. You could build up from 10 to 12 to 14 km per week, and then rest with a 10 km week before moving on to 16 km. Don't allow yourself to get caught up by the thrill of increasing your distance every single week. That simply can't work for very long.

4. **Make haste slowly**

   Another cause of injury and fatigue is increasing the speed of your training runs too much and too often. The same is true of interval workouts, hill running and racing. When the time is right for faster-paced running (once you're completely comfortable with the amount of training you're doing), ease into it just once a week. Don't run fast more than twice a week. Balance your fast workouts and your long runs (both qualify as "hard" days) with slower, shorter days. This is the well-known and widely followed "hard/easy" system.

5. **Strive for efficient running form**

   You'll have more fun if you aren't struggling against yourself. Poor running form is the cause of many injuries. For example, running too high on the toes or leaning too far forward can contribute to shin splints and Achilles tendonitis. Carrying the arms too high or swinging the elbows too far back can cause problems in your back and shoulders. To run efficiently, keep your body straight and concentrate on lifting your knee just enough to allow your leg to swing forward naturally. Combined with a gentle heel landing, this will give you an economical yet productive stride.

6. **Choose wholesome foods**

   Runners function best on a diet high in complex carbohydrates. That means eating plenty of fruits, vegetables, whole-grain products and low-fat dairy foods. Avoid fried foods, pastries, cookies, ice cream and other fat-laden items. Fish, lean meats and poultry are better for you than their high-fat cousins—sausage, bacon, untrimmed red meats and cold cuts. Fluids are vital: aim to drink 8 to 10 glasses of water a day.

7. Practice proper form on hills

When climbing hills, shorten your stride and concentrate on lifting your knees and landing more on the front of your foot. Pump your arms like a cross-country skier. Lean forward but keep your back straight, your hips in, your chest out and your head up. Downhill sections require careful consideration as well, since the additional momentum can increase your chance of injury. Hold your arms low and tilt your body forward to keep it perpendicular to the slope. Allow your stride to stretch out a little, but don't exaggerate it. Try to avoid the braking action of landing too hard on your heels.

8. Be smart about injuries

Runners who interrupt their training programs at the first sign of injury generally recover very quickly. You might not be able to enter the race you're aiming for, but you'll be able to find another one soon. On the other hand, runners who persist in training hard even after they start to break down are courting much more serious injuries. When you develop a persistent running pain, open your eyes and obey the red flag. Stop. Rest. Wait until your body is ready to begin training again. When it is, ease back into your training. Don't try to catch up too quickly—it can't be done.

9. Pay attention to pain

It's usually okay to forget mild discomfort if it goes away during a run and doesn't return after. But pain that worsens during a run or that returns after each run cannot be ignored. Remember, pain has a purpose. It's a warning sign from your body that something is wrong. Don't overlook it. Instead, change your running pattern, or if the pain is severe enough, stop running and seek professional help.

For more training tips follow John Stanton and the Running Room online at **www.runningroom.com** or on social media.

www.facebook.com/runningroominc
www.facebook.com/JohnStantonRunningRoom

www.twitter.com/RunningRoom
www.twitter.com/JohnStantonRR

Google+ Running Room
Google+ John Stanton

Conditioning Programs

Chapter 2

Beginner's Conditioning Program

If you are just beginning, start first with walking and add running later. If you have been inactive for a long time, start with a walking program. Walk before you run. Think of it as a pre-conditioning program.

Start with a fast walk for 20 to 30 minutes. Slow down if you find yourself short of breath. Don't stop. Keep moving. By pumping your arms as you walk and really stepping out, you can increase your heart rate to a level nearly equivalent to a slow run. Also, by walking vigorously uphill, you can add to the rigour of your walking workouts.

Once you can walk briskly for 30 minutes, you can start interspersing some easy running into your walking. By slowly exchanging running for walking, over several weeks you will gradually progress to running for 10 minutes and walking for 1 minute.

The following schedule should be run at least three times per week. All running should be done at a conversation pace, and all walking should be done briskly. Of course, a proper warm-up and cool-down are required. Start and end all sessions with a one-minute walk.

Training Rules

1. This program starts conservatively. You can even fall a little behind and still get back on track easily.

2. Once you reach the halfway mark, you may find it difficult to keep up unless you run faithfully at least three times a week.

3. If you can't keep up or lose time from illness or injury, don't panic. Stay at the level you can handle or go back a level until you are ready to move on.

4. Remember, it took you years to get out of shape; take your time getting back into shape.

Your Goal: The Beginner's Conditioning Program is designed to get you running using the run-walk approach for varying distances.

Conditioning Program - Beginner Running

Week	Training Session	Total Exercise Time	
		Running	Walking
1	Walk 1 min; Run 1 min/Walk 2 min x 6 sets; Run 1 min; Walk 1 min	7 min	14 min
2	Walk 1 min; Run 2 min/Walk 1 min x 10 sets	10 min	11 min
3	Walk 1 min; Run 2 min/Walk 1 min x 6 sets; Run 2 min; Walk 1 min	14 min	8 min
4	Walk 1 min; Run 3 min/Walk 1 min x 5 sets	15 min	6 min
5	Walk 1 min; Run 4 min/Walk 1 min x 4 sets	16 min	5 min
6	Walk 1 min; Run 5 min/Walk 1 min x 3 sets; Run 2 min; Walk 1 min	17 min	5 min
7	Walk 1 min; Run 6 min/Walk 1 min x 3 sets	18 min	4 min
8	Walk 1 min; Run 8 min/Walk 1 min x 2 sets; Run 2 min; Walk 1 min	18 min	4 min
9	Walk 1 min; Run 10 min/Walk 1 min x 2 sets	20 min	3 min
10	Walk 1 min; Run 10 min/Walk 1 min x 2 sets	20 min	3 min

Intermediate Running Conditioning Program

After you can run five minutes nonstop, you are ready for the intermediate program. This phase of training requires that you stay at the level of running for five minutes, but at a frequency of three to five times a week, for three to four weeks.

Note: When you have reached 30 minutes, three times per week, pause. Hold your running at this level and concentrate on gradually bringing your running time up to 30 minutes on the other days that you are running. You are progressing well, and you don't want to risk injury, fatigue or boredom.

Conditioning Program - Intermediate Running

Week	Training Session	Sessions	Total Exercise Time Running	Walking
1	Walk 1 min; Run 5 min/Walk 1 min x 4 sets	3	20 min	5 min
2	Walk 1 min; Run 7 min/Walk 1 min x 3 sets	3	21 min	4 min
3	Walk 1 min; Run 10 min/Walk 1 min x 2 sets	3	20 min	3 min
4	Walk 1 min; Run 10 min/Walk 1 min x 2 sets	3	20 min	3 min
5	Walk 1 min; Run 10 min/Walk 1 min x 2 sets	3	20 min	3 min
6	Walk 1 min; Run 10 min/Walk 1 min x 2 sets; Run 2 min; Walk 1 min	3	22 min	4 min
7	Walk 1 min; Run 10 min/Walk 1 min x 2 sets; Run 4 min; Walk 1 min	3	24 min	4 min
8	Walk 1 min; Run 10 min/Walk 1 min x 2 sets; Run 6 min; Walk 1 min	3	26 min	4 min
9	Walk 1 min; Run 10 min/Walk 1 min x 2 sets; Run 8 min; Walk 1 min	3	28 min	4 min
	Walk 1 min; Run 10 min/Walk 1 min x 2 sets	1	20 min	3 min
10	Walk 1 min; Run 10 min/Walk 1 min x 3 sets	3	30 min	4 min
	Walk 1 min; Run 10 min/Walk 1 min x 2 sets	1	20 min	3min

Advanced 5 K Conditioning Program

If you can currently run 20 minutes or longer on a consistent basis, you are ready for the advanced 5 K program. This program focuses on safely increasing your total running time or distance as well as adding in extra days of training.

After you have reached week 10, when you are running five times a week, hold your longest runs up to 30 minutes and concentrate on gradually bringing your other runs up to 30 minutes as well.

Conditioning Program - Advanced Running

			Total Exercise Time	
Week	Training Session	Sessions	Running	Walking
1	Walk 1 min; Run 10 min/Walk 1 min x 2 sets	3	20 min	3 min
2	Walk 1 min; Run 10 min/Walk 1 min x 2 sets; Run 2 min; Walk 1 min	3	22 min	4 min
3	Walk 1 min; Run 10 min/Walk 1 min x 2 sets; Run 4 min; Walk 1 min	3	24 min	4 min
4	Walk 1 min; Run 10 min/Walk 1 min x 2 sets; Run 6 min; Walk 1 min	3	26 min	4 min
5	Walk 1 min; Run 10 min/Walk 1 min x 2 sets; Run 8 min; Walk 1 min	3	28 min	4 min
6	Walk 1 min; Run 10 min/Walk 1 min x 3 sets	3	30 min	4 min
	Walk 1 min; Run 10 min/Walk 1 min x 2 sets	1	20 min	3 min
7	Walk 1 min; Run 10 min/Walk 1 min x 3 sets	3	30 min	4 min
	Walk 1 min; Run 10 min/Walk 1 min x 2 sets; Run 2 min; Walk 1 min	1	22 min	4 min
8	Walk 1 min; Run 10 min/Walk 1 min x 3 sets; Run 3 min; Walk 1 min	3	33 min	5 min
	Walk 1 min; Run 10 min/Walk 1 min x 2 sets; Run 2 min; Walk 1 min	1	22 min	4 min
9	Walk 1 min; Run 10 min/Walk 1 min x 3 sets; Run 3 min; Walk 1 min	3	33 min	5 min
	Walk 1 min; Run 10 min/Walk 1 min x 2 sets; Run 4 min; Walk 1 min	1	24 min	4 min
10	Walk 1 min; Run 10 min/Walk 1 min x 3 sets	2	30 min	4 min
	Walk 1 min; Run 10 min/Walk 1 min x 2 sets; Run 5 min; Walk 1 min	2	25 min	4 min
	Walk 1 min; Run 10 min/Walk 1 min x 2 sets	1	20 min	3 min

Running Form

Chapter 3

One of the most frequent questions from runners is: how can I improve my form? Before getting into a discussion about form or giving advice, I usually suggest that the person come with me to the finish area of a local road race to watch the lead runners come in. It is always apparent that in the lead pack, as in the whole pack, there are some runners with great-looking form and some with ugly form. I encourage the person to look past each runner's form and instead notice the degree of relaxation. The lead runners are certainly fast (after all, they are in the lead at the finish), but they also maintain a relaxed form, even under race conditions.

If you go down to a local track and listen in on the comments of a running coach, the number one thing you will hear during a workout is: "Relax." The coach will be making all kinds of points, but the basic message to the runners—no matter how hard they are pushing—is to relax.

So, remember to relax, and let's take a look at other ways to improve your running form.

Posture

Have a friend video you as you run—both at the start and near the end of a long run. You will end up with a valuable tool to assess any running posture problems. Here are some of the most common problems as well as some tips on how to improve them.

Overstriding

Increase the rhythm of your arm swing and concentrate on shortening your swing. Think of running on hot coals to shorten your reach with each foot stride forward.

Tightness in Shoulders

Learn to relax the palms of your hands by gently touching your thumb to the middle finger. Your fingers should be loose, so make sure you do not grip a fist as you run. Practice running with a couple of soda crackers held in your hands. Cup your hands with your thumbs on top.

Knee Lift

Your knees should be lifted just high enough to clear the ground. Too high a knee lift wastes energy—most runners are training for a forward-motion sport.

Arm Carriage

Holding the palms of your hands inward and slightly upward will keep your elbows near your sides. Your arm swing should be in the general area of your heart. Too high an arm swing results in your heart having to pump uphill. Think of the words "relaxed" and "rhythmic." Increasing your arm swing can help improve the turnover rate of tired legs.

Too Much Bounce

Look at the horizon and concentrate on keeping your head in the same plane. Do some accelerations with an increased body lean. Focus on lower knee lift and try to think of reaching with your arms rather than pumping them.

Perfect Form

There really is no perfect form. The important thing is to stay relaxed, stay rhythmic and push hard. Much of your running form is a gift from your parents, but you can make the most of your gift with some attention to fine tuning your individual form.

Form Tips

1. Stay Upright

Good running posture is simply good body posture. When the head, shoulders and hips are all lined up over the feet, you can move forward as a unit, with a minimum amount of effort.

2. Chest Forward

Many runners let their chest sag into a slouch. In such a position, the lungs can't maximize their efficiency. Before starting your run, relax and take a deep breath, which moves the lungs into an efficient position. After you exhale, maintain the chest in this beneficial alignment. The most efficient way to run is to have your head, neck and shoulders erect. When you run leaning forward, you're always fighting gravity.

3. Hips Forward

One of the most common errors is letting the hips shift back and the butt stick out behind you. Taking a deep breath often pulls the hips forward and into an alignment that allows for easier running.

4. The Foot Plant

There is a difference between what should happen and what you may be able to control. First, let your shoe professional fit you with shoes that are right for you, since modern training shoes are designed to accommodate biomechanically different feet. Then, just start running! Your personal stride is the result of your shape, your physique and the strength and balance of your muscles below your waist. Please don't try to change your foot plant as you train: you will not be running naturally and you are likely to cause more problems than you solve. Changes to your gait only happen as a result of longer-term changes elsewhere. As you gain fitness and strength, you may notice that many irregularities resolve themselves. If you do have a problem that continues to affect your activity, you may have to seek the advice of a therapist or coach to address your particular situation.

5. Arms

Arm position can vary widely from one runner to the next. In general, the arms should swing naturally and loosely from the shoulders—not too high and not too low. This usually means staying relaxed. Staying relaxed will prevent the arms from being carried too high, which will expend more energy than needed. Your hands should never cross the centre of your chest. Remember, you want your body to go forward and not side-to-side, thus your arms should do the same. Keep your hands in a relaxed position and try not to clench them into fists.

6. Stride Length

As a coach, my experience has shown that as runners get faster, their stride length shortens. Leg turnover rate, or the cadence of the runner's legs, is the key to faster and more efficient running. Staying light on your feet with a more rapid leg turnover rate will keep many of the aches, pains and injuries away.

Sprinters have a high knee lift. Anyone running more than a mile needs to minimize knee lift. If your knees go too high, you are overusing the quadriceps muscles on the front of the thigh. This overstriding leaves the runner with sore quadriceps at the end of the run. Keep your leg turnover light and rapid—more of a shuffle than a sprinter's stride.

Stay relaxed with a low, short stride. This will prevent tightness in the shin, behind the knee or in the back of the thigh. Kicking too far forward tightens up the lower leg and hamstrings.

Do short accelerations while staying light on your feet. Keep your foot strike quieter with each stride, keeping your foot close to the ground to prevent any excessive bouncing.

7. Head and Neck

Your torso will normally do what your head is doing. If you are dropping your head down, your torso will probably follow and lean too far forward. Keep the neck and shoulders relaxed. Try not to hunch your shoulders, which will cause undue fatigue to that area. Your eyes should be looking about 20 to 30 metres ahead of you.

8. Practice Your Technique

Once or twice a week, a little technique work is really helpful. After your warm-up, run some accelerations of 50 to 150 metres. Pick one of the elements of good form and feel yourself executing it well during the acceleration. Rehearse each element at least four times, and limit yourself to one or two elements in each session. A change in technique may feel a little awkward at first, but you'll know when you've got it right, because it will feel so good! For athletes in events like sprinting and hurdling, effective technique is a vitally important ingredient of success. Their warm-up is actually designed so that their technique (they often call it "skill") is rehearsed every time they prepare for training or competition. Your warm-up consists of a period of jogging and stretching. Build in some technique accelerations, too. They take very little extra time. You'll get the most effective "motor learning" by focusing on one point of technique for a short period of time and repeating it several times. When you're moving your body in a new way, your body gets tired quickly. You'll feel it and there will be a noticeable loss in your coordination and motor skill. It's temporary, though—the short break between accelerations will give you the recovery time you need.

Photo: Scott Soulis

Proper Shoe Selection

Chapter 4

Shoes are a runner's most important piece of equipment. The average runner strikes the ground with a force of three and a half to five times his or her weight, which has to be absorbed by the feet and legs. The right pair of running shoes can accommodate your individual needs, enhance your performance, prevent injuries and keep you running comfortably.

Determining Your Foot Type

After your heel strikes the ground in a running stride, your foot pronates by rolling inward and flattening out. Your foot then supinates (rotates outward) after the weight is transferred to the ball of your foot. The foot then becomes a rigid lever so that you may propel yourself forward. Perfect running styles are rare. Overpronation is more common than oversupination.

The Overpronator - *Figure 1*

- Feet roll inward too much when running
- Generally has low arches
- Knees and kneecaps move towards the inside of the feet when bending at the knees
- More susceptible to runner's knee, iliotibial band syndrome, tendonitis and plantar fasciitis

The Supinator / Under Pronator - *Figure 2*

- Lacks normal inward rolling of feet when running
- Generally has high arches
- Knees and kneecaps move towards the outside of the feet when bending at the knees
- More susceptible to ankle sprains, stress fractures, plantar fasciitis and pain on the outside of the shin or knee

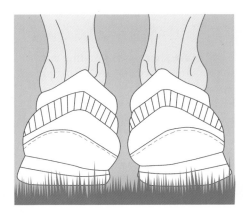 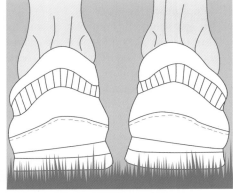

Figure 1 - Overpronation   **Figure 2** - Supination / Under Pronation

Reading Old Shoes

Your old shoes reveal a lot about what type of runner you are. If you walk into a Running Room or Walking Room to buy a new pair of running shoes, a staff member can often put you into the right pair in a matter of moments. Most magicians would never reveal the secrets of their trade, but I can take some of the mystery out of shoe selection with a few tips on how to read your old shoes.

View the upper of the shoe from the rear:

- The shoe's centerline should be perpendicular to the ground.
- The centerline shifts inward, to the medial side of the shoe, if the runner has overpronated.
- The centerline shifts outward, to the lateral side of the shoe, if the runner has supinated.

Check the condition of the midsoles:

- The midsole compresses uniformly if the runner has normal pronation.
- The midsole compresses more on the inside of the shoe if the runner has overpronated.
- The midsole compresses more on the outside of the shoe if the runner has supinated.

Check the wear on the upper:

- The upper retains its shape if the runner has normal pronation.
- The upper sags inward from the toe area if the runner overpronates during push-off.

Guidelines to Find the Best Shoe Fit

- Shop in the afternoon to get the right fit.
- Try on both shoes with the same type of sock that will be worn during the activity.
- Try on several different models to make a good comparison.
- Walk or jog around the store in the shoes.
- Check the quality of the shoes. Look at the stitching, eyelets and gluing. Feel for bumps inside the shoe.
- The sole should flex only where your foot flexes.
- Your toes should not be pressing against the end of the shoe when standing nor should there be too much room (a centimetre or more). Shoes that are too big or too small can cause injury to the toenails while running.
- The heel counter should fit snugly so that there is no slipping at the heel.
- Shoes should be comfortable on the day you buy them. Don't rely on a break-in period.
- Consult the staff at the Running Room for help in selecting the correct shoe.

Shoe Classifications

1. Neutral - Underpronator

You need cushioning, a flexible forefoot and no motion control features.

Underpronator - Neutral

- Feet and ankles roll to the outside
- Arches are high and/or rigid
- Knee remains in a neutral position or moves outwards through foot strike
- Shoe wears along the outside of the sole

Neutral Features

- Best Last: Curved-lasted shoe for low or moderate rear stability
- Best Shoes: Neutral shoes with a flexible forefoot and soft/firm midsole

2. Stability - Normal Pronator

You need extra cushioning and some degree of stability, but you are not an excessive pronator.

Normal Pronator

- Normal sized arch; runner lands on the outside of the heel and moderately rolls inward (pronates)
- Semi-flexible arch that requires varied degrees of support
- Knees roll slightly in when bent

Stability Features

- Best Last: Semi Curved
- Best Shoes: Stability shoes with moderate control features, such as moderate pronation control, moderate heel counters and a multi-density midsole. These features also provide extra cushioning and an excellent degree of stability.

3. Motion Control - Overpronator

You overpronate and quickly break down midsoles—you need a firm midsole with a sturdy heel counter.

Overpronator

- Feet and ankles roll in (pronate) excessively
- Low/flat arches
- Knees move inwards when bending
- Midsole of shoe breaks down quickly

Motion Control Features

- Best Last: Straight or semi-curved for maximum rearfoot stability
- Best Shoes: Motion Control or strong stability shoes with firm midsole. A wide landing base and control features, such as a strong, rigid heel counter keep the heel secure and reduces the degree and rate of pronation. Additional extended multi-density posting on the medial side adds motion control.

How To Stretch

Chapter 5

Warm-up, Stretching and Cool-down

Along with aerobic fitness and strength, flexibility is also an important component of total body health and wellness. It is traditionally believed that performing warm-up exercises that include stretching can help prevent injury during the subsequent activity. Although this may not be completely true, a well-planned warm-up, cool-down and stretching regimen are valuable elements of every training session.

The Purpose of Warm-up

The main purpose of the warm-up is to ready the body for the upcoming activity. It assists the heart, lungs and muscles to prepare for the intensity of exercise and to ease the body through the transition from rest to exercise. The best format for your warm-up is to do your planned exercise activity, only much more slowly, for the first few minutes of your session.

The Purpose of Cool-down

The cool-down is the exact opposite of the warm-up. Incorporating a planned cool-down at the end of your exercise session assists your body in the transition from exercise to rest. It allows the heart to adjust to the decreased intensity more slowly and can prevent laboured breathing at the end of higher intensity exercise sessions. The optimal length of the cool-down period is dependent on the intensity and duration of the prior exercise. A cool-down period of 5 to 10 minutes should suffice for almost every workout. As in the warm-up, the activities performed during the cool-down should be the same as the exercise session, only slower or on a smaller scale.

Stretching

It is best to stretch when the muscles are warm. If your preference is to stretch before you work out, then be sure to do a full warm-up first. On the other hand, stretching can be a useful part of an extended cool-down. If improved flexibility is your goal, then stretching while your muscles are warm from a training session will give the best results. Stretching is only recommended after an appropriate cool-down.

How to Stretch

Stretching should be done slowly, without bouncing. Stretch to where you feel a slight, easy stretch (not pain). Hold this feeling for approximately 20 seconds. As you hold the stretch, the feeling of tension should diminish. If it doesn't, ease off slightly into a more comfortable stretch. This easy first stretch readies the tissue for the developmental stretch. After holding the easy stretch, move slightly farther into the stretch until you feel mild tension again. This is the developmental stretch, which should be held for 20 to 30 seconds. The feeling of stretch tension should slightly diminish or stay the same. If the tension increases or becomes painful, you are overstretching. Again, ease off to a comfortable stretch.

The developmental stretch reduces the risk of injury and will safely increase flexibility. Hold the stretch at a tension that feels comfortable to you. The key to stretching is to stay relaxed while you concentrate on the area being stretched. Do not hold your breath—keep your breathing regular. Don't worry about how far you can stretch in comparison to others—increased personal flexibility is a guaranteed result of a regular stretching program.

The Stretches

The following are recommended stretches for beginner and novice runners.

Calf - *Figure 1a, 1b*

Stand about 3 ft. (1 m) from a wall, railing or tree with your feet flat on the ground, toes slightly turned inward, heels out and back straight. The forward leg should be bent and the rear leg should be gradually straightened until there is tension in the calf *(Figure 1a)*. Finally, bend the straight leg at the knee to work closer to the Achilles tendon *(Figure 1b)*.

Hamstring - *Figure 2a, 2b*

Lie down on your back with one knee bent and your foot flat on the ground. Slip a Thera-Band under your other foot, and grab the ends in your hands while keeping your knee bent *(Figure 2a)*. Slowly straighten this leg *(Figure 2b)*. Feel the stretch. Repeat with the other leg.

Quadriceps ("quads") - *Figure 3*

Place one arm on something handy to balance yourself and use the other hand to pull the foot back when one leg is bent at the knee. The bent knee should touch the other knee. Don't push it forward or pull it back. While this stretch is being executed, the belly button should be pulled up under the rib cage, which is called a pelvic tilt. The tilt protects the back.

Iliotibial Band - *Figure 4*

With one leg towards a railing, bench or wall and the other leg slightly bent, cross the leg to be stretched behind the bent leg. Shift your hip towards the wall to stretch the iliotibial band. You should feel the stretch over the hip area.

Buttocks - *Figure 5*

Sit up straight with one leg straight and the knee of your other leg bent. Place the foot of the bent leg on the outside of the straightened leg. Slowly pull the bent leg towards the opposing shoulder. The buttock of the bent leg will be stretched.

Hip Flexor - *Figure 6a, 6b*

Kneel on one knee and place the other leg forward at a 90-degree stance *(Figure 6a)*. Keep the back straight and maintain the pelvic tilt while lunging forward *(Figure 6b)*. The rear knee is planted to stretch the hip in front.

Figure 2a - Hamstring Position 1

Figure 1a - Calf Position 1   **Figure 1b -** Calf Position 2   **Figure 2b -** Hamstring Position 2

Figure 5 - Buttocks

Figure 3 - Quadriceps   **Figure 4** - Iliotibial Band

Figure 6a - Hip Flexor Position 1   **Figure 6b** - Hip Flexor Position 2

Weather and Safety

Chapter 6

Weather and Running

Unfortunately, every running day will not be a nice fall morning or a brisk spring evening, so preparation is necessary. What do you wear? How do you alter your training schedule? How do you protect yourself from the elements? See below for tips on coping with various weather conditions.

Cold Weather

Keep a few simple rules in mind if you are going out in cold weather:

1. Understand that if it is -30°C (-22°F) or colder, you do not have to be a hero. Find an alternative to running outside. This could be a great day for cross-training.

2. Wear three layers: a base layer, an insulating layer and a windproof shell. Some clothing (such as Fit-Wear) is quite efficient, so if you have this type of clothing, two layers will suffice.

3. Do not expose too much skin. Keep all extremities covered (such as your ears, hands, wrists, ankles and neck). Your respiratory area (nose and mouth) will stay warm thanks to your breathing.

4. Apply Bodyglide or another type of body lubricant to any exposed skin to help protect it from the wind and the drying effects of the cold.

5. Run in small loops close to your home base. If you find it is getting unbearable, you will not be too far away from shelter.

6. Bring cab fare, a cell phone and I.D.

7. Tell someone where you are going (route map) and give that person an idea of your approximate time of arrival.

8. If you start to detect frostbite, seek shelter immediately and warm up. Do not stay out any longer.

Hot Weather

Heat is one of the endurance athlete's greatest enemies. Heat stress does not need to progress very far before it becomes a medical emergency. Luckily, we have defense mechanisms that protect us. At the first sign of any symptoms, stop, cool off and seek help. Symptoms may include no longer sweating, dizziness, chills and disorientation. Your cooling mechanism operates on water. In hot conditions, you need to drink frequently before, during and after exercise. If you feel thirsty, you are already dehydrated. For the length of normal fitness activities, plain water is your most effective drink. Sports drinks work best immediately after you have finished.

Here are some precautions that will make your hot-weather running safer:

1. Drink at least two cups of water before and a cup for every 15 to 20 minutes during your run.

2. Water is the best drink for exercise lasting less than three hours. For workouts over three hours in duration, a sports drink will replace lost electrolytes and provide some fuel (sugar) for exercise. If you are going to use a commercial sports drink during a race, be sure to try it in training.

3. Wear a vented cap, sun visor, sunglasses and protective sunscreen. If you are sun-sensitive or concerned about sun exposure, wear some of the new long-sleeved CoolMax or Fit-Wear shirts. They are both sun-safe and cool.

4. Lubricate your underarms and inner thighs. Gentlemen should apply Bodyglide to their nipples and ladies should add it at the bra line. Doing so will reduce chafing, a common problem in the summer months.

5. Avoid consuming alcoholic beverages. They will only make you feel warmer as their calories are burned quickly, raising your metabolic rate and body temperature. Alcohol is a diuretic and brings on the risk of dehydration.

6. Adjust your intensity to the temperature. In extreme conditions, slow down your pace.

7. Increase your intake of vitamin C. It is a natural and effective defense against heat stroke, cramps, prickly heat rash and exhaustion.

8. Let someone know your route if you are running alone. Better still, run with a buddy—you'll run with less intensity and it will be more social.

9. If you plan to race on a hot-weather holiday, give yourself four to five days to adjust to the heat.

10. Early mornings are the best time to run. Sunset runs can catch you out in the dark.

11. Water running can be very social and a cool, high-quality workout.

12. Include lots of fruit in your diet. Watermelon, oranges, bananas and strawberries are a good way to take in vitamin C and potassium, two nutrients that are lost through sweat.

13. If you finish your run and you are still outside, take extra clothes with you to avoid being chilled.

14. Savour the odd low-fat frozen treat to reward yourself for keeping the daily workout fun!

15. Skim milk is also a great cool drink, and it is very low in fat.

Safety

We are always at risk in today's world, but there are a number of things we can do to make our runs safer. Some of these tips will seem strange to people in some areas, and all too poignant for others.

1. Carry identification. Carry your name and address, a friend or relative's telephone number and your blood type on the inside sole of your running shoe or tied to a lace. Include other relevant medical information.

2. Carry the appropriate coins for an emergency telephone call, or carry a cell phone.

3. Don't wear jewelry.

4. Make sure your friends or relatives know your favourite running routes. Leave the route written down somewhere. If possible, inform someone of which route you are running.

5. Run in familiar areas and alter your route pattern. Know the location of telephones, businesses and stores on your route.

6. Avoid unpopulated areas, deserted streets and overgrown trails. Especially avoid unlit areas at night. Steer clear of parked cars and bushes.

7. Stay alert. The more aware you are, the less vulnerable you are.

8. Don't wear headphones. Use your hearing to be conscious of your surroundings.

9. Ignore verbal harassment. Use discretion in acknowledging strangers.

10. Look directly at others and be observant. Keep your distance and keep moving.

11. Run against traffic, so you can easily see approaching automobiles.

12. Wear reflective material if you must run before or after dark.

13. Use your intuition about suspicious persons and areas.

14. Carry a whistle or noisemaker.

15. Call the police immediately if something happens to you or if you notice anything out of the ordinary during your run.

Race Day

Chapter 7

Rule #1: Relax!

The best advice for first-time racers is to relax and enjoy yourself. Racing is meant to be a stimulating, memorable experience. You will enjoy the experience more if you keep things in perspective and use common sense. Even if something goes wrong in your first race—like getting stomach cramps or having your shoelaces come untied—it's not the end of the world. You'll live to run and race again.

Race Day Tips for Rookies

1. Your Goal

Your goal is simply to finish. Your first race is for the experience, not for the competition. Run it knowing your time will be a personal record.

2. Eating and Drinking

On race day, don't eat or drink anything out of the ordinary. This is not the time to experiment, no matter what you may have heard about athletic superfoods. Nor do you have follow the carbohydrate loading strategy employed by marathon runners. In fact, for your last meal (taken at least three hours before the race start) you might want to eat less than normal, since nervousness could upset your digestive system.

In warm weather, drink 500 mL of water one hour before the start, and continue drinking every 10 minutes during the race. You should practice the same routine during hot-weather training runs. Don't forget that heat can kill. Don't try to be a hero if you are racing in hot weather. Adjust your expectations and drink fluids at regular intervals to counteract the water loss from your perspiration and breathing.

3. Strategy

Planning your race strategy in advance will build your confidence. Break the course into small sections, making sure you know the locations of hills and other key landmarks. It's particularly useful to be familiar with the last half-kilometre of the course, where you will be budgeting your energy for the finish. On race day, it's a good idea to warm up by running the last half-kilometre of the course and setting a few landmarks in your mind.

4. Getting Ready

When you arrive at the race, don't be intimidated by what you see other runners doing. Many of them are preparing for a hard effort, whereas you want to save your energy for a comfortable race. Do some walking, some stretching and some light jogging to loosen up.

5. Lining Up and Starting

Make your way to the back of the pack where you won't get caught in the starting sprint. Many marathons have pacing groups: join the group that will be running at a pace you feel comfortable with. Begin slowly. Don't worry about all the runners who take off ahead of you. It's far better to start slowly and catch up later than to begin too fast and be passed by hundreds of runners after a kilometre or two. Once you have room to run freely, move into your normal, relaxed training pace. Maintain that pace (the one that allows you to talk comfortably) at least until you reach the halfway mark. At that point, if you feel strong and want to pick it up, go ahead—but make sure you do it gradually. If you reach a point of struggle, slow down to gather your strength.

6. Walking

Use the strategy of running 10 minutes and walking 1 minute. Nowhere on the entry form does it say that you can't walk. So if you feel the need, take a walk break, particularly on the hills. Disguise your walking breaks by calling them water breaks. Since drinking water is so important during a race, many runners stop and drink when they get to the water tables. You can do the same—getting water plus the rest you need—and no one will be the wiser.

7. Finishing

Keep your pace constant and steady. Don't sprint hard at the finish line. That is not only unwise, but it can be dangerous. Concentrate on finishing with good, strong, relaxed form. Enjoy the moment!

8. Recovery

After you finish, be sure to walk around for a cool-down. Drink plenty of fluids, especially if it's a hot day. Change into dry clothes as soon as possible, and when you get home, stretch your muscles thoroughly after taking a cool shower. Don't do any running the next day, although it's okay to swim or bike. You might find it hard to contain your newfound racing enthusiasm, but running on tired leg muscles only tempts injury.

Training Programs

Chapter 8

On the following pages you will find a variety of suggested training schedules. These schedules have been designed to help runners to complete the event and/or to achieve specific time goals. At the bottom of every training schedule, you will see a chart outlining the pace requirements for each run.

Training Program Workouts

Long Slow Distance (LSD) Run/Walk

Long Slow Distance runs are the cornerstone of any distance training program. Take a full minute to walk for every 10 minutes of running. These runs are designed to be much slower than race pace (60–70% of your maximum heart rate), so don't be overly concerned with your pace. These runs help to increase the capillary network in your body and raise your anaerobic threshold. They also mentally prepare you for long races.

A Note on LSD Pace

The pace for the long run on the chart includes the walk time. This program provides an upper end (slow) and bottom end (fast) pace to use as a guideline. The upper end pace is preferable because it will keep you injury-free. Running at the bottom end pace is a common mistake made by many runners. They try to run at the maximum pace, which is an open invitation to injury. I know very few runners who have been injured from running too slowly, but loads of runners who incurred injuries by running too fast. In the early stages of the program, it is very easy to run the long runs too fast, but like the marathon or half marathon, the long runs require discipline and patience. Practice your sense of pace by slowing the long runs down. You will recover faster and avoid injuries.

Steady Run

The steady run is a run below targeted race pace (70% of your maximum heart rate). Run at a comfortable speed; if in doubt, go slowly. The run is broken down into components of running and walking. We encourage you to use the run/walk approach. Walk breaks are a great way to stay consistent in your training.

Hills

Distance for the day is calculated as the approximate distance covered up and down the hill. Now, you will no doubt have to run to the hill and back from the hill unless of course you drive to the hill. You will need to add your total warm-up and cool-down distance to the totals noted on the training schedule. I recommend a distance of 3 km both ways to ensure adequate warm-up and recovery, because hills put a lot of stress on the body. Hills are run at tempo pace (80% of your maximum heart rate) and must include a heart rate recovery to 120 beats per minute at the bottom of each hill repeat.

Tempo

Before starting tempo runs, include several weeks of hill running to improve your strength, form and confidence. For the tempo runs, run at 80% of your maximum heart rate for 60–80% of your planned race distance to improve your coordination and leg turnover rate. Include a warm-up and cool-down of three to five minutes. These runs simulate race conditions and the effort required on race day.

Fartlek (Speed Play)

Fartlek runs are spontaneous runs over varying distances and intensity. Run the short bursts at 70–80% of your maximum heart rate, if you are wearing a monitor. Conversation is possible, but you should notice an increase in breathing, heart rate and perspiration. Between these short bursts of hard effort (which are no longer than three minutes), add recovery periods of easy running to bring your heart rate down to 120 beats per minute. Speed play fires up your performance, and the added recovery / rest interval keeps the session attainable and fun.

Walk Adjusted Race Pace

How do we arrive at a "Walk Adjusted" race pace? When you are walking, you are moving more slowly than your "average run pace". When you are running, you are moving faster than your "average walk pace". The "Walk Adjusted" race pace factors in the variation in walking and running speed. The challenge is how to find the average speed of your walking pace. We have devised a formula to calculate moderate walk pace, which allows us to determine the exact splits including running and walking pace. The effect of this calculation is that the "Walk Adjusted" race pace is faster per kilometre than the average race pace. However, when calculated with your walk pace, you will end up with your target race pace. You can go online at www.runningroom.com and print out your "Walk Adjusted" pace bands for race day.

Training Rules

- When you are selecting and designing a program to fit your lifestyle, write down your planned distance or time for a certain day.
- In the weeks following a race, you may need to reduce your mileage to help with recovery.
- Do not attempt to combine long runs and races on the same day or weekend.

Conditioning Program - 5K Race
(Recorded in minutes)

Week	Sun	Mon	Tues	Wed	Thu	Fri	Sat	Total Time
1	25 min	Off	Off	25 min	Off	25 min	Off	Run/Walk 1h 15 min
Workout: Run 5 min/Walk 1 min x 4 sets; Walk 1 min = 25 min								
2	25 min	Off	Off	25 min	Off	25 min	Off	Run/Walk 1h 15 min
Workout: Run 7 min/Walk 1 min x 3 sets; Walk 1 min = 25 min								
3	23 min	Off	Off	23 min	Off	23 min	Off	Run/Walk 1h 09 min
Workout: Run 10 min/Walk 1 min x 2 sets; Walk 1 min = 23 min								
4	23 min	Off	Off	23 min	Off	23 min	Off	Run/Walk 1h 09 min
Workout: Run 10 min/Walk 1 min x 2 sets; Walk 1 min = 23 min								
5	26 min	Off	Off	26 min	Off	26 min	Off	Run/Walk 1h 18 min
Workout: Run 10 min/Walk 1 min x 2 sets; Walk 1 min, Run 2 min; Walk 1 min = 26 min								
6	28 min	Off	Off	28 min	Off	28 min	Off	Run/Walk 1h 24 min
Workout: Run 10 min/Walk 1 min x 2 sets; Walk 1 min, Run 2 min; Walk 1 min = 28 min								
7	29 min	Off	Off	29 min	Off	29 min	Off	Run/Walk 1h 27 min
Workout: Run 10 min/Walk 1 min x 2 sets; Walk 1 min, Run 5 min; Walk 1 min = 29 min								
8	30 min	Off	Off	30 min	Off	30 min	Off	Run/Walk 1h 30 min
Workout: Run 10 min/Walk 1 min x 2 sets; Walk 1 min, Run 6 min; Walk 1 min = 30 min								
9	32 min	Off	Off	32 min	Off	32 min	Off	Run/Walk 1h 36 min
Workout: Run 10 min/Walk 1 min x 2 sets; Walk 1 min, Run 8 min; Walk 1 min = 32 min								
10	23 min	Off	34 min	34 min	Off	34 min	Off	Run/Walk 2h 05 min
Workout: Run 10 min/Walk 1 min x 2 sets; Walk 1 min = 23 min Workout: Run 10 min/Walk 1 min x 3 sets, Walk 1 min = 34 min								
11	Race Day 5K Run 10 min/Walk 1 min							Run/Walk 0:30 - 0:40

Pace Schedule

Don't worry about pace or distance as the goal is to increase the interval of time running / walking.

Week 1 will incorporate 5 min Run/1 min Walk.
Week 2 will increase to 7 min Run/1 min Walk.

All other weeks will progress to the formula of 10 min Run/1 min Walk

Conditioning Program - 10 K Race
(Recorded in kilometres)

Week	Sun	Mon	Tues	Wed	Thu	Fri	Sat	Total
1	Off	Off	3 Run/Walk	4 Run/Walk	Off	3 Run/Walk	Off	Run/Walk 10
2	5 LSD Run/Walk	Off	3 Run/Walk	4 Run/Walk	Off	3 Run/Walk	Off	Run/Walk 15
3	6 LSD Run/Walk	Off	4 Run/Walk	4 Run/Walk	Off	4 Run/Walk	Off	Run/Walk 18
4	7 LSD Run/Walk	Off	4 Run/Walk	4 Run/Walk	Off	4 Run/Walk	Off	Run/Walk 19
5	8 LSD Run/Walk	Off	3 Run/Walk	3 Hills (400 m Hills) 2.5 km	Off	4 Run/Walk	Off	Run/Walk 17.5
6	8 LSD Run/Walk	Off	3 Run/Walk	4 Hills (400 m Hills) 3 km	Off	4 Run/Walk	Off	Run/Walk 18
7	8 LSD Run/Walk	Off	3 Run/Walk	5 Hills (400 m Hills) 4 km	Off	5 Run/Walk	Off	Run/Walk 20
8	9 LSD Run/Walk	Off	3 Run/Walk	6 Hills (400 m Hills) 5 km	Off	5 Run/Walk	Off	Run/Walk 22
9	10 LSD Run/Walk	Off	4 Run/Walk	5 Run/Walk	Off	4 Run/Walk	Off	Run/Walk 23
10	6 LSD Run/Walk	Off	3 Run/Walk	5 Run/Walk	Off	3 Run/Walk	Off	Run/Walk 17
11	10 K Race							Run/Walk 10

Pace Schedule	Don't worry about pace here. The goal is simply to build your training base. Run/Walk interval = Run 10 min/Walk 1 min

42

To Complete - Half Marathon
(Recorded in kilometres)

Week	Sun	Mon	Tues	Wed	Thu	Fri	Sat	Total
1	Off	Off	Off	3 Steady Run	3 Steady Run	Off	3 Steady Run	9
2	7 LSD Run/Walk	Off	4 Steady Run	3 Steady Run	3 Steady Run	Off	3 Steady Run	20
3	7 LSD Run/Walk	Off	4 Steady Run	3 Steady Run	4 Steady Run	Off	3 Steady Run	21
4	7 LSD Run/Walk	Off	3 Steady Run	4 Steady Run	3 Steady Run	Off	4 Steady Run	21
5	9 LSD Run/Walk	Off	4 Steady Run	3 Steady Run	3 Steady Run	Off	3 Steady Run	22
6	9 LSD Run/Walk	Off	5 Steady Run	3 Steady Run	4 Steady Run	Off	3 Steady Run	24
7	10 LSD Run/Walk	Off	4 Steady Run	3 Hills 2.5 km	5 Steady Run	Off	3 Steady Run	24.5
8	10 LSD Run/Walk	Off	4 Steady Run	4 Hills 3 km	5 Steady Run	Off	4 Steady Run	26
9	12 LSD Run/Walk	Off	4 Steady Run	5 Hills 4 km	6 Steady Run	Off	4 Steady Run	30
10	14 LSD Run/Walk	Off	4 Steady Run	6 Hills 5 km	6 Steady Run	Off	5 Steady Run	34
11	16 LSD Run/Walk	Off	5 Steady Run	7 Hills 5.5 km	7 Steady Run	Off	5 Steady Run	38.5
12	16 LSD Run/Walk	Off	5 Steady Run	8 Hills 6 km	7 Steady Run	Off	6 Steady Run	40
13	12 LSD Run/Walk	Off	5 Steady Run	9 Hills 7 km	8 Steady Run	Off	6 Steady Run	38
14	18 LSD Run/Walk	Off	6 Steady Run	6 Fartlek	8 Steady Run	Off	6 Steady Run	44
15	18 LSD Run/Walk	Off	6 Steady Run	4 Fartlek	8 Steady Run	Off	6 Steady Run	42
16	20 LSD Run/Walk	Off	6 Steady Run	4 Fartlek	8 Steady Run	Off	6 Steady Run	44
17	6 LSD Run/Walk	Off	10 Steady Run	6 Steady Run	Off	Off	3 Steady Run	25
18	Race - Half Marathon							21.1

Pace Schedule	LSD Run	Steady Run	Tempo/ Fartlek/Hills	Speed	Race	Walk Adjusted Race Pace
To Complete	9:29 - 10:33	9:29	8:37	7:36	8:32	8:21

Run/Walk Interval = Run 10 min/Walk 1 min
Hills are a distance of 400 m

To Complete - Marathon
(Recorded in kilometres)

Week	Sun	Mon	Tues	Wed	Thu	Fri	Sat	Total
1	10 LSD Run/Walk	Off	6 Tempo	10 Tempo	6 Steady Run	Off	6 Steady Run	38
2	10 LSD Run/Walk	Off	6 Tempo	10 Tempo	6 Steady Run	Off	6 Steady Run	38
3	13 LSD Run/Walk	Off	6 Tempo	10 Tempo	8 Steady Run	Off	6 Steady Run	43
4	13 LSD Run/Walk	Off	6 Tempo	10 Tempo	8 Steady Run	Off	6 Steady Run	43
5	16 LSD Run/Walk	Off	6 Tempo	10 Tempo	8 Steady Run	Off	6 Steady Run	46
6	16 LSD Run/Walk	Off	6 Tempo	10 Tempo	8 Steady Run	Off	6 Steady Run	46
7	19 LSD Run/Walk	Off	6 Tempo	4 Hills 5 km	8 Steady Run	Off	6 Steady Run	44
8	23 LSD Run/Walk	Off	6 Tempo	5 Hills 6 km	8 Steady Run	Off	6 Steady Run	49
9	26 LSD Run/Walk	Off	6 Tempo	6 Hills 7 km	8 Steady Run	Off	6 Steady Run	53
10	19 LSD Run/Walk	Off	6 Tempo	7 Hills 8.5 km	8 Steady Run	Off	6 Steady Run	47.5
11	29 LSD Run/Walk	Off	6 Tempo	8 Hills 9.5 km	8 Steady Run	Off	6 Steady Run	58.5
12	29 LSD Run/Walk	Off	6 Tempo	9 Hills 11 km	8 Steady Run	Off	6 Steady Run	60
13	32 LSD Run/Walk	Off	6 Tempo	10 Hills 12 km	8 Steady Run	Off	6 Steady Run	64
14	23 LSD Run/Walk	Off	6 Tempo	10 Fartlek	8 Steady Run	Off	6 Steady Run	53
15	29 LSD Run/Walk	Off	6 Tempo	10 Fartlek	10 Steady Run	Off	6 Steady Run	61
16	32 LSD Run/Walk	Off	6 Tempo	10 Fartlek	10 Steady Run	Off	6 Steady Run	64
17	23 LSD Run/Walk	Off	6 Tempo	10 Fartlek	10 Steady Run	Off	16 Steady Run	65
18	6 Run/Walk	Off	6 Tempo	10 Steady Run	Off	Off	3 Steady Run	25
19	Race - Marathon							42.2

Pace Schedule	LSD Run	Steady Run	Tempo/ Fartlek/Hills	Speed	Race	Walk Adjusted Race Pace
To Complete	8:34 - 9:37	8:37	7:48	6:51	7:49	7:36

Run/Walk Interval = Run 10 min/Walk 1 min
Hills are a distance of 600 m

Using the Diary
Chapter 9

Overview

This training diary is intended to help you train better, race better, and record your progress towards your goals. You will receive a special joy, along with a sense of personal reflection, when you keep a handwritten diary of your running. By tracking your daily training, you are much more likely to remain committed to your training goals and you will be better able to identify factors that contribute to injury or overtraining.

Vitals

Tracking your daily vitals will help you identify trends that contribute to possible overtraining and help you establish a baseline for factors that positively influence your training. Monitor your resting heart rate and watch for elevations that may indicate fatigue or overtraining. Changes in your weight should always be monitored in order to maintain your ideal weight. Rapid weight loss or weight gain should always be viewed as a sign of potential health issues and should alert you to confer with your doctor. Sleep affects us all differently, but we all have a base level of sleep we need to function daily and to maintain a training schedule. Watch for changes in sleep patterns, because restless or poor sleep may be another indicator of overtraining.

Recording Heart Rate Information

Resting Heart Rate (RHR)

Heart rate is expressed as beats per minute (bpm). The RHR is a person's heart rate at rest—the lowest number of heartbeats per minute at complete rest. The best time to find out your resting heart rate is in the morning, after a good night's sleep, before you get out of bed.

On average, the heart beats about 60 to 80 times a minute when we're at rest, but for top athletes it can be below 30 bpm. RHR usually rises with age, and it generally decreases as your fitness level increases.

RHR is used to determine your training Target Heart Rate (THR). Athletes sometimes measure their RHR as one way to find out if they're overtrained. An exceptionally high RHR may be a sign of over-exertion or illness.

Average Heart Rate (AHR)

The Average Heart Rate figure (in bpm) is a calculation of your average heart rate during your last workout. You can use this measurement to determine the effectiveness of your exercise program and see your progress.

Target Heart Rate (THR)

The Target Heart Rate is a heart rate range that a person aims for when exercising. Target heart rate zones are expressed as percentages of a person's maximum heart rate (MHR). Target heart rate lets you measure your initial fitness level and monitor your progress in a fitness program. For a rough estimate of your maximum heart rate (MHR), subtract your age from 220. For first-time exercisers, have your physician perform a stress test to determine your MHR along with your target zones specific to your goal. This is especially important if you are just starting an exercise program or have not exercised for a prolonged period of time. In our book, *Running Room's Book on Running*, we have an extensive chapter on heart rate training and establishing target heart rate levels.

Why is establishing daily THR so important?

The most effective way to reach your fitness goal is to exercise in your target heart rate zone. There is a target zone that is right for each day's workout. For example, if you want to improve aerobic fitness, you need to be working at 70–80% of your MHR, for 40 to 60 minutes per day, 3 to 4 times per week. Without this information, you would get on a treadmill and not know how hard or how long you should be exercising. Our friends at Polar Canada (a company specializing in heart rate monitors) have suggested three key target zones to help you achieve specific goals:

60–70%	Lose Weight or Recover
70–80%	Improve Aerobic Fitness
80+ %	Increase Athletic Performance

Improving Overall Fitness

If you have reached a plateau, you should begin to alter the frequency, intensity and duration of your workouts. The body is smart and adapts to routine. If you follow the same program, and have done so for a while, you may have stopped seeing results. Variety is the key. Focus on different workouts, at different target zones, on different days while adjusting your workout time.

Workout Gear

Make notes about the gear you wear, because it does affect the quality of your workout. Use this section to track the mileage on your shoes, to ensure you are not training on a shoe that has come to the end of its life cycle. Training on shoes that have lost their cushioning and support will inevitably result in injury. Although we all vary in terms of how long we can train on a pair of shoes, we suggest that shoes be retired from "active training" after 800 km.

Notes

As this is a training diary, use this section for personal notes and comments about the workout or to indicate who your training partner was on this day. This provides valuable clues about good or bad training and also can be fun to review months or years later.

Weekly Summary Graph

We have provided a great little graphing tool to allow you to see your week at a glance. If you're making a bar graph, you can choose to track your time or your distance. Mark an appropriate scale on the left side of the grid and fill in the bar for each day of training.

If you're creating a line graph, try using two different ink colours to track both distance (using the left margin) and time (using the right margin).

Sample Time or Distance Bar Graph

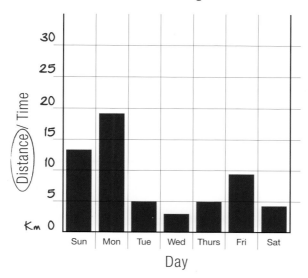

Total Time: _____   Total Distance: __58 km__

Sample Combined Time and Distance Line Graph

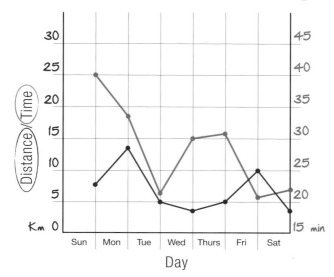

Total Time: 1hr 32 min   Total Distance: __45 km__

Sunday

Date: _____ **Week 1**

Vitals: **Resting HR:** _____ bpm   **Weight:** _____ kg/lbs   Hours Slept: _____ hrs

Sport: _____   Workout: _____

Course: _____   Duration: _____   Distance: _____

Intensity: ☐ **Maximum**   ☐ **Hard**   ☐ **Medium**   ☐ **Minimum**

Average HR: _____ bpm   Target HR: _____ bpm

Feeling: ☐ **Fantastic**   ☐ **Good**   ☐ **Difficult**   ☐ **Very Difficult**

Weather   Temperature: _____ ° ___   Workout Gear: _____

Notes:

Monday

Date: _____ **Week 1**

Vitals: **Resting HR:** _____ bpm   **Weight:** _____ kg/lbs   Hours Slept: _____ hrs

Sport: _____   Workout: _____

Course: _____   Duration: _____   Distance: _____

Intensity: ☐ **Maximum**   ☐ **Hard**   ☐ **Medium**   ☐ **Minimum**

Average HR: _____ bpm   Target HR: _____ bpm

Feeling: ☐ **Fantastic**   ☐ **Good**   ☐ **Difficult**   ☐ **Very Difficult**

Weather   Temperature: _____ ° ___   Workout Gear: _____

Notes:

Tuesday

Date: _____ **Week 1**

Vitals: **Resting HR:** _____ bpm   **Weight:** _____ kg/lbs   Hours Slept: _____ hrs

Sport: _____   Workout: _____

Course: _____   Duration: _____   Distance: _____

Intensity: ☐ **Maximum**   ☐ **Hard**   ☐ **Medium**   ☐ **Minimum**

Average HR: _____ bpm   Target HR: _____ bpm

Feeling: ☐ **Fantastic**   ☐ **Good**   ☐ **Difficult**   ☐ **Very Difficult**

Weather   Temperature: _____ ° ___   Workout Gear: _____

Notes:

Wednesday

Date: _____ **Week 1**

Vitals: **Resting HR:** _____ bpm **Weight:** _____ kg/lbs Hours Slept: _____ hrs

Sport: _____ Workout: _____

Course: _____ Duration: _____ Distance: _____

Intensity: ☐ **Maximum** ☐ **Hard** ☐ **Medium** ☐ **Minimum**

Average HR: _____ bpm Target HR: _____ bpm

Feeling: ☐ **Fantastic** ☐ **Good** ☐ **Difficult** ☐ **Very Difficult**

Weather Temperature: _____ ° ___ Workout Gear: _____

Notes:

Thursday

Date: _____ **Week 1**

Vitals: **Resting HR:** _____ bpm **Weight:** _____ kg/lbs Hours Slept: _____ hrs

Sport: _____ Workout: _____

Course: _____ Duration: _____ Distance: _____

Intensity: ☐ **Maximum** ☐ **Hard** ☐ **Medium** ☐ **Minimum**

Average HR: _____ bpm Target HR: _____ bpm

Feeling: ☐ **Fantastic** ☐ **Good** ☐ **Difficult** ☐ **Very Difficult**

Weather Temperature: _____ ° ___ Workout Gear: _____

Notes:

Friday

Date: _____ **Week 1**

Vitals: **Resting HR:** _____ bpm **Weight:** _____ kg/lbs Hours Slept: _____ hrs

Sport: _____ Workout: _____

Course: _____ Duration: _____ Distance: _____

Intensity: ☐ **Maximum** ☐ **Hard** ☐ **Medium** ☐ **Minimum**

Average HR: _____ bpm Target HR: _____ bpm

Feeling: ☐ **Fantastic** ☐ **Good** ☐ **Difficult** ☐ **Very Difficult**

Weather Temperature: _____ ° ___ Workout Gear: _____

Notes:

Saturday

Date: _____   **Week 1**

Vitals: **Resting HR**: _____ bpm   **Weight**: _____ kg/lbs   Hours Slept: _____ hrs

Sport: _____   Workout: _____

Course: _____   Duration: _____   Distance: _____

Intensity: ☐ **Maximum**   ☐ **Hard**   ☐ **Medium**   ☐ **Minimum**

Average HR: _____ bpm   Target HR: _____ bpm

Feeling: ☐ **Fantastic**   ☐ **Good**   ☐ **Difficult**   ☐ **Very Difficult**

Weather   Temperature: _____ ° ___   Workout Gear: _____

Notes: _____

_____

Weekly Summary

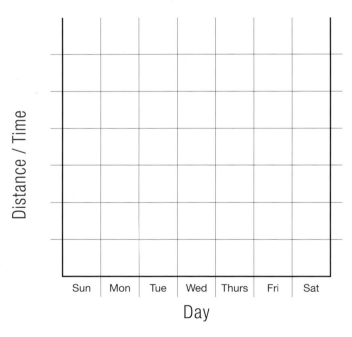

Total Time: _____   Total Distance: _____

Additional Information: _____

_____

_____

_____

50

WHOEVER SAID
money can't buy you happiness
NEEDS TO RUN IN A
BRAND-NEW PAIR OF SHOES.

- JOHN STANTON

Sunday
Date: _____   **Week 2**

Vitals: **Resting HR**: _____ bpm   **Weight**: _____ kg/lbs   Hours Slept: _____ hrs

Sport: _____   Workout: _____

Course: _____   Duration: _____   Distance: _____

Intensity: □ **Maximum**   □ **Hard**   □ **Medium**   □ **Minimum**

Average HR: _____ bpm   Target HR: _____ bpm

Feeling: □ **Fantastic**   □ **Good**   □ **Difficult**   □ **Very Difficult**

Weather   Temperature: _____ ° ___   Workout Gear: _____

Notes:
_____
_____

Monday
Date: _____   **Week 2**

Vitals: **Resting HR**: _____ bpm   **Weight**: _____ kg/lbs   Hours Slept: _____ hrs

Sport: _____   Workout: _____

Course: _____   Duration: _____   Distance: _____

Intensity: □ **Maximum**   □ **Hard**   □ **Medium**   □ **Minimum**

Average HR: _____ bpm   Target HR: _____ bpm

Feeling: □ **Fantastic**   □ **Good**   □ **Difficult**   □ **Very Difficult**

Weather   Temperature: _____ ° ___   Workout Gear: _____

Notes:
_____
_____

Tuesday
Date: _____   **Week 2**

Vitals: **Resting HR**: _____ bpm   **Weight**: _____ kg/lbs   Hours Slept: _____ hrs

Sport: _____   Workout: _____

Course: _____   Duration: _____   Distance: _____

Intensity: □ **Maximum**   □ **Hard**   □ **Medium**   □ **Minimum**

Average HR: _____ bpm   Target HR: _____ bpm

Feeling: □ **Fantastic**   □ **Good**   □ **Difficult**   □ **Very Difficult**

Weather   Temperature: _____ ° ___   Workout Gear: _____

Notes:
_____
_____

Wednesday

Date: **Week 2**

Vitals: **Resting HR:** _____ bpm   **Weight:** _____ kg/lbs   Hours Slept: _____ hrs

Sport: _____   Workout: _____

Course: _____   Duration: _____   Distance: _____

Intensity: ☐ **Maximum**   ☐ **Hard**   ☐ **Medium**   ☐ **Minimum**

Average HR: _____ bpm   Target HR: _____ bpm

Feeling: ☐ **Fantastic**   ☐ **Good**   ☐ **Difficult**   ☐ **Very Difficult**

Weather   Temperature: _____ ° ___   Workout Gear: _____

Notes:

Thursday

Date: **Week 2**

Vitals: **Resting HR:** _____ bpm   **Weight:** _____ kg/lbs   Hours Slept: _____ hrs

Sport: _____   Workout: _____

Course: _____   Duration: _____   Distance: _____

Intensity: ☐ **Maximum**   ☐ **Hard**   ☐ **Medium**   ☐ **Minimum**

Average HR: _____ bpm   Target HR: _____ bpm

Feeling: ☐ **Fantastic**   ☐ **Good**   ☐ **Difficult**   ☐ **Very Difficult**

Weather   Temperature: _____ ° ___   Workout Gear: _____

Notes:

Friday

Date: **Week 2**

Vitals: **Resting HR:** _____ bpm   **Weight:** _____ kg/lbs   Hours Slept: _____ hrs

Sport: _____   Workout: _____

Course: _____   Duration: _____   Distance: _____

Intensity: ☐ **Maximum**   ☐ **Hard**   ☐ **Medium**   ☐ **Minimum**

Average HR: _____ bpm   Target HR: _____ bpm

Feeling: ☐ **Fantastic**   ☐ **Good**   ☐ **Difficult**   ☐ **Very Difficult**

Weather   Temperature: _____ ° ___   Workout Gear: _____

Notes:

Saturday

Date: _____   **Week 2**

Vitals: **Resting HR:** _____ bpm   **Weight:** _____ kg/lbs   Hours Slept: _____ hrs

Sport: _____   Workout: _____

Course: _____   Duration: _____   Distance: _____

Intensity: ☐ **Maximum**   ☐ **Hard**   ☐ **Medium**   ☐ **Minimum**

Average HR: _____ bpm   Target HR: _____ bpm

Feeling: ☐ **Fantastic**   ☐ **Good**   ☐ **Difficult**   ☐ **Very Difficult**

Weather   Temperature: _____ ° ____   Workout Gear: _____

Notes: _____

_____

Weekly Summary

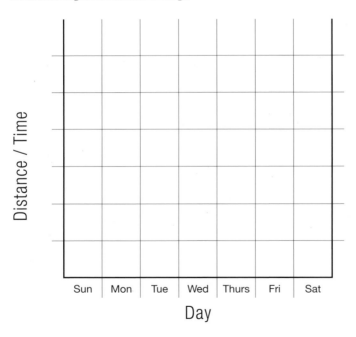

Total Time: _____   Total Distance: _____

Additional Information: _____

_____

_____

_____

YOU HAVE TO HAVE A *dream*
SO YOU CAN GET UP IN THE
morning.
– BILLY WILDER

Sunday

Date: _____   **Week 3**

Vitals: **Resting HR:** _____ bpm   **Weight:** _____ kg/lbs   Hours Slept: _____ hrs

Sport: _____   Workout: _____

Course: _____   Duration: _____   Distance: _____

Intensity: ☐ **Maximum**   ☐ **Hard**   ☐ **Medium**   ☐ **Minimum**

Average HR: _____ bpm   Target HR: _____ bpm

Feeling: ☐ **Fantastic**   ☐ **Good**   ☐ **Difficult**   ☐ **Very Difficult**

Weather   Temperature: _____ ° ___   Workout Gear: _____

Notes: _____

_____

Monday

Date: _____   **Week 3**

Vitals: **Resting HR:** _____ bpm   **Weight:** _____ kg/lbs   Hours Slept: _____ hrs

Sport: _____   Workout: _____

Course: _____   Duration: _____   Distance: _____

Intensity: ☐ **Maximum**   ☐ **Hard**   ☐ **Medium**   ☐ **Minimum**

Average HR: _____ bpm   Target HR: _____ bpm

Feeling: ☐ **Fantastic**   ☐ **Good**   ☐ **Difficult**   ☐ **Very Difficult**

Weather   Temperature: _____ ° ___   Workout Gear: _____

Notes: _____

_____

Tuesday

Date: _____   **Week 3**

Vitals: **Resting HR:** _____ bpm   **Weight:** _____ kg/lbs   Hours Slept: _____ hrs

Sport: _____   Workout: _____

Course: _____   Duration: _____   Distance: _____

Intensity: ☐ **Maximum**   ☐ **Hard**   ☐ **Medium**   ☐ **Minimum**

Average HR: _____ bpm   Target HR: _____ bpm

Feeling: ☐ **Fantastic**   ☐ **Good**   ☐ **Difficult**   ☐ **Very Difficult**

Weather   Temperature: _____ ° ___   Workout Gear: _____

Notes: _____

_____

Wednesday

Date: _____   **Week 3**

Vitals: **Resting HR:** _____ bpm   **Weight:** _____ kg/lbs   Hours Slept: _____ hrs

Sport: _____   Workout: _____

Course: _____   Duration: _____   Distance: _____

Intensity: ☐ **Maximum**   ☐ **Hard**   ☐ **Medium**   ☐ **Minimum**

Average HR: _____ bpm   Target HR: _____ bpm

Feeling: ☐ **Fantastic**   ☐ **Good**   ☐ **Difficult**   ☐ **Very Difficult**

Weather   Temperature: _____ ° ___   Workout Gear: _____

Notes:

_____

_____

Thursday

Date: _____   **Week 3**

Vitals: **Resting HR:** _____ bpm   **Weight:** _____ kg/lbs   Hours Slept: _____ hrs

Sport: _____   Workout: _____

Course: _____   Duration: _____   Distance: _____

Intensity: ☐ **Maximum**   ☐ **Hard**   ☐ **Medium**   ☐ **Minimum**

Average HR: _____ bpm   Target HR: _____ bpm

Feeling: ☐ **Fantastic**   ☐ **Good**   ☐ **Difficult**   ☐ **Very Difficult**

Weather   Temperature: _____ ° ___   Workout Gear: _____

Notes:

_____

_____

Friday

Date: _____   **Week 3**

Vitals: **Resting HR:** _____ bpm   **Weight:** _____ kg/lbs   Hours Slept: _____ hrs

Sport: _____   Workout: _____

Course: _____   Duration: _____   Distance: _____

Intensity: ☐ **Maximum**   ☐ **Hard**   ☐ **Medium**   ☐ **Minimum**

Average HR: _____ bpm   Target HR: _____ bpm

Feeling: ☐ **Fantastic**   ☐ **Good**   ☐ **Difficult**   ☐ **Very Difficult**

Weather   Temperature: _____ ° ___   Workout Gear: _____

Notes:

_____

_____

Saturday

Date: _____ Week 3

Vitals: **Resting HR:** _____ bpm   **Weight:** _____ kg/lbs   Hours Slept: _____ hrs

Sport: _____   Workout: _____

Course: _____   Duration: _____   Distance: _____

Intensity: ☐ **Maximum**   ☐ **Hard**   ☐ **Medium**   ☐ **Minimum**

Average HR: _____ bpm Target HR: _____ bpm

Feeling: ☐ **Fantastic**   ☐ **Good**   ☐ **Difficult**   ☐ **Very Difficult**

Weather   Temperature: _____ ° ___   Workout Gear: _____

Notes: _____

_____

_____

Weekly Summary

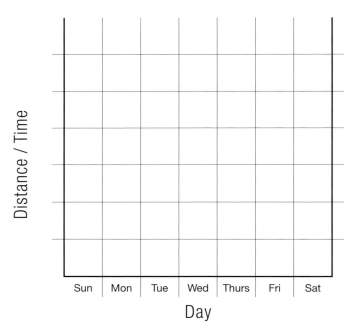

Total Time: _____   Total Distance: _____

Additional Information: _____

_____

_____

_____

_____

NO ONE IS BORN A RUNNER—
YOU BECOME ONE.

– JOHN STANTON

Sunday

Date: _____   **Week 4**

Vitals: **Resting HR**: _____ bpm   **Weight**: _____ kg/lbs   Hours Slept: _____ hrs

Sport: _____   Workout: _____

Course: _____   Duration: _____   Distance: _____

Intensity: ☐ **Maximum**   ☐ **Hard**   ☐ **Medium**   ☐ **Minimum**

Average HR: _____ bpm   Target HR: _____ bpm

Feeling: ☐ **Fantastic**   ☐ **Good**   ☐ **Difficult**   ☐ **Very Difficult**

Weather   Temperature: _____ ° ___   Workout Gear: _____

Notes: _____

_____

Monday

Date: _____   **Week 4**

Vitals: **Resting HR**: _____ bpm   **Weight**: _____ kg/lbs   Hours Slept: _____ hrs

Sport: _____   Workout: _____

Course: _____   Duration: _____   Distance: _____

Intensity: ☐ **Maximum**   ☐ **Hard**   ☐ **Medium**   ☐ **Minimum**

Average HR: _____ bpm   Target HR: _____ bpm

Feeling: ☐ **Fantastic**   ☐ **Good**   ☐ **Difficult**   ☐ **Very Difficult**

Weather   Temperature: _____ ° ___   Workout Gear: _____

Notes: _____

_____

Tuesday

Date: _____   **Week 4**

Vitals: **Resting HR**: _____ bpm   **Weight**: _____ kg/lbs   Hours Slept: _____ hrs

Sport: _____   Workout: _____

Course: _____   Duration: _____   Distance: _____

Intensity: ☐ **Maximum**   ☐ **Hard**   ☐ **Medium**   ☐ **Minimum**

Average HR: _____ bpm   Target HR: _____ bpm

Feeling: ☐ **Fantastic**   ☐ **Good**   ☐ **Difficult**   ☐ **Very Difficult**

Weather   Temperature: _____ ° ___   Workout Gear: _____

Notes: _____

_____

Wednesday

Date: _____   **Week 4**

Vitals: **Resting HR:** _____ bpm **Weight:** _____ kg/lbs Hours Slept: _____ hrs

Sport: _____ Workout: _____

Course: _____ Duration: _____ Distance: _____

Intensity: ☐ **Maximum** ☐ **Hard** ☐ **Medium** ☐ **Minimum**

Average HR: _____ bpm Target HR: _____ bpm

Feeling: ☐ **Fantastic** ☐ **Good** ☐ **Difficult** ☐ **Very Difficult**

Weather Temperature: _____ ° ___ Workout Gear: _____

Notes: _____

_____

Thursday

Date: _____   **Week 4**

Vitals: **Resting HR:** _____ bpm **Weight:** _____ kg/lbs Hours Slept: _____ hrs

Sport: _____ Workout: _____

Course: _____ Duration: _____ Distance: _____

Intensity: ☐ **Maximum** ☐ **Hard** ☐ **Medium** ☐ **Minimum**

Average HR: _____ bpm Target HR: _____ bpm

Feeling: ☐ **Fantastic** ☐ **Good** ☐ **Difficult** ☐ **Very Difficult**

Weather Temperature: _____ ° ___ Workout Gear: _____

Notes: _____

_____

Friday

Date: _____   **Week 4**

Vitals: **Resting HR:** _____ bpm **Weight:** _____ kg/lbs Hours Slept: _____ hrs

Sport: _____ Workout: _____

Course: _____ Duration: _____ Distance: _____

Intensity: ☐ **Maximum** ☐ **Hard** ☐ **Medium** ☐ **Minimum**

Average HR: _____ bpm Target HR: _____ bpm

Feeling: ☐ **Fantastic** ☐ **Good** ☐ **Difficult** ☐ **Very Difficult**

Weather Temperature: _____ ° ___ Workout Gear: _____

Notes: _____

_____

Saturday

Date: _____   **Week 4**

Vitals: **Resting HR**: _____ bpm   **Weight**: _____ kg/lbs   Hours Slept: _____ hrs

Sport: _____   Workout: _____

Course: _____   Duration: _____   Distance: _____

Intensity: ☐ **Maximum**   ☐ **Hard**   ☐ **Medium**   ☐ **Minimum**

Average HR: _____ bpm   Target HR: _____ bpm

Feeling: ☐ **Fantastic**   ☐ **Good**   ☐ **Difficult**   ☐ **Very Difficult**

Weather   Temperature: _____ ° ___   Workout Gear: _____

Notes: _____

_____

Weekly Summary

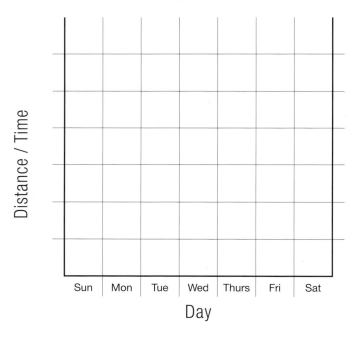

Total Time: _____   Total Distance: _____

Additional Information: _____

_____

_____

_____

_____

DON'T TAKE ANYONE ELSE'S DEFINITION OF *success* AS YOUR OWN.

-Jacueline Briskin

Sunday

Date: _____   **Week 5**

Vitals: **Resting HR**: _____ bpm   **Weight**: _____ kg/lbs   Hours Slept: _____ hrs

Sport: _____   Workout: _____

Course: _____   Duration: _____   Distance: _____

Intensity: ☐ **Maximum**   ☐ **Hard**   ☐ **Medium**   ☐ **Minimum**

Average HR: _____ bpm   Target HR: _____ bpm

Feeling: ☐ **Fantastic**   ☐ **Good**   ☐ **Difficult**   ☐ **Very Difficult**

Weather   Temperature: _____ ° ___   Workout Gear: _____

Notes: _____

_____

Monday

Date: _____   **Week 5**

Vitals: **Resting HR**: _____ bpm   **Weight**: _____ kg/lbs   Hours Slept: _____ hrs

Sport: _____   Workout: _____

Course: _____   Duration: _____   Distance: _____

Intensity: ☐ **Maximum**   ☐ **Hard**   ☐ **Medium**   ☐ **Minimum**

Average HR: _____ bpm   Target HR: _____ bpm

Feeling: ☐ **Fantastic**   ☐ **Good**   ☐ **Difficult**   ☐ **Very Difficult**

Weather   Temperature: _____ ° ___   Workout Gear: _____

Notes: _____

_____

Tuesday

Date: _____   **Week 5**

Vitals: **Resting HR**: _____ bpm   **Weight**: _____ kg/lbs   Hours Slept: _____ hrs

Sport: _____   Workout: _____

Course: _____   Duration: _____   Distance: _____

Intensity: ☐ **Maximum**   ☐ **Hard**   ☐ **Medium**   ☐ **Minimum**

Average HR: _____ bpm   Target HR: _____ bpm

Feeling: ☐ **Fantastic**   ☐ **Good**   ☐ **Difficult**   ☐ **Very Difficult**

Weather   Temperature: _____ ° ___   Workout Gear: _____

Notes: _____

_____

Wednesday

Date: _____   **Week 5**

Vitals: **Resting HR**: _____ bpm   **Weight**: _____ kg/lbs   Hours Slept: _____ hrs

Sport: _____   Workout: _____

Course: _____   Duration: _____   Distance: _____

Intensity: ☐ **Maximum**   ☐ **Hard**   ☐ **Medium**   ☐ **Minimum**

Average HR: _____ bpm   Target HR: _____ bpm

Feeling: ☐ **Fantastic**   ☐ **Good**   ☐ **Difficult**   ☐ **Very Difficult**

Weather   Temperature: _____ ° ___   Workout Gear: _____

Notes:

_____

_____

Thursday

Date: _____   **Week 5**

Vitals: **Resting HR**: _____ bpm   **Weight**: _____ kg/lbs   Hours Slept: _____ hrs

Sport: _____   Workout: _____

Course: _____   Duration: _____   Distance: _____

Intensity: ☐ **Maximum**   ☐ **Hard**   ☐ **Medium**   ☐ **Minimum**

Average HR: _____ bpm   Target HR: _____ bpm

Feeling: ☐ **Fantastic**   ☐ **Good**   ☐ **Difficult**   ☐ **Very Difficult**

Weather   Temperature: _____ ° ___   Workout Gear: _____

Notes:

_____

_____

Friday

Date: _____   **Week 5**

Vitals: **Resting HR**: _____ bpm   **Weight**: _____ kg/lbs   Hours Slept: _____ hrs

Sport: _____   Workout: _____

Course: _____   Duration: _____   Distance: _____

Intensity: ☐ **Maximum**   ☐ **Hard**   ☐ **Medium**   ☐ **Minimum**

Average HR: _____ bpm   Target HR: _____ bpm

Feeling: ☐ **Fantastic**   ☐ **Good**   ☐ **Difficult**   ☐ **Very Difficult**

Weather   Temperature: _____ ° ___   Workout Gear: _____

Notes:

_____

_____

Saturday

Date: _____   **Week 5**

Vitals: **Resting HR**: _____ bpm   **Weight**: _____ kg/lbs   Hours Slept: _____ hrs

Sport: _____   Workout: _____

Course: _____   Duration: _____   Distance: _____

Intensity: ☐ **Maximum**   ☐ **Hard**   ☐ **Medium**   ☐ **Minimum**

Average HR: _____ bpm   Target HR: _____ bpm

Feeling: ☐ **Fantastic**   ☐ **Good**   ☐ **Difficult**   ☐ **Very Difficult**

Weather   Temperature: _____ ° ___   Workout Gear: _____

Notes: _____

_____

Weekly Summary

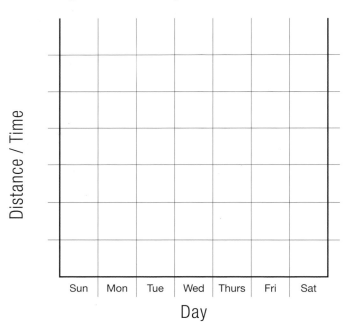

Total Time: _____   Total Distance: _____

Additional Information: _____

_____

_____

_____

Treat each day as a
new challenge.

You can achieve any
intelligent goal that
you set for
yourself.

—John Stanton

Sunday

Date: _____   **Week 6**

Vitals: **Resting HR**: _____ bpm   **Weight**: _____ kg/lbs   Hours Slept: _____ hrs

Sport: _____   Workout: _____

Course: _____   Duration: _____   Distance: _____

Intensity: ☐ **Maximum**   ☐ **Hard**   ☐ **Medium**   ☐ **Minimum**

Average HR: _____ bpm   Target HR: _____ bpm

Feeling: ☐ **Fantastic**   ☐ **Good**   ☐ **Difficult**   ☐ **Very Difficult**

Weather   Temperature: _____ ° ___   Workout Gear: _____

Notes: _____

_____

Monday

Date: _____   **Week 6**

Vitals: **Resting HR**: _____ bpm   **Weight**: _____ kg/lbs   Hours Slept: _____ hrs

Sport: _____   Workout: _____

Course: _____   Duration: _____   Distance: _____

Intensity: ☐ **Maximum**   ☐ **Hard**   ☐ **Medium**   ☐ **Minimum**

Average HR: _____ bpm   Target HR: _____ bpm

Feeling: ☐ **Fantastic**   ☐ **Good**   ☐ **Difficult**   ☐ **Very Difficult**

Weather   Temperature: _____ ° ___   Workout Gear: _____

Notes: _____

_____

Tuesday

Date: _____   **Week 6**

Vitals: **Resting HR**: _____ bpm   **Weight**: _____ kg/lbs   Hours Slept: _____ hrs

Sport: _____   Workout: _____

Course: _____   Duration: _____   Distance: _____

Intensity: ☐ **Maximum**   ☐ **Hard**   ☐ **Medium**   ☐ **Minimum**

Average HR: _____ bpm   Target HR: _____ bpm

Feeling: ☐ **Fantastic**   ☐ **Good**   ☐ **Difficult**   ☐ **Very Difficult**

Weather   Temperature: _____ ° ___   Workout Gear: _____

Notes: _____

_____

Wednesday

Date: _____   **Week 6**

Vitals: **Resting HR**: _____ bpm   **Weight**: _____ kg/lbs   Hours Slept: _____ hrs

Sport: _____   Workout: _____

Course: _____   Duration: _____   Distance: _____

Intensity: ☐ **Maximum**   ☐ **Hard**   ☐ **Medium**   ☐ **Minimum**

Average HR: _____ bpm   Target HR: _____ bpm

Feeling: ☐ **Fantastic**   ☐ **Good**   ☐ **Difficult**   ☐ **Very Difficult**

Weather   Temperature: _____ ° ___   Workout Gear: _____

Notes:

Thursday

Date: _____   **Week 6**

Vitals: **Resting HR**: _____ bpm   **Weight**: _____ kg/lbs   Hours Slept: _____ hrs

Sport: _____   Workout: _____

Course: _____   Duration: _____   Distance: _____

Intensity: ☐ **Maximum**   ☐ **Hard**   ☐ **Medium**   ☐ **Minimum**

Average HR: _____ bpm   Target HR: _____ bpm

Feeling: ☐ **Fantastic**   ☐ **Good**   ☐ **Difficult**   ☐ **Very Difficult**

Weather   Temperature: _____ ° ___   Workout Gear: _____

Notes:

Friday

Date: _____   **Week 6**

Vitals: **Resting HR**: _____ bpm   **Weight**: _____ kg/lbs   Hours Slept: _____ hrs

Sport: _____   Workout: _____

Course: _____   Duration: _____   Distance: _____

Intensity: ☐ **Maximum**   ☐ **Hard**   ☐ **Medium**   ☐ **Minimum**

Average HR: _____ bpm   Target HR: _____ bpm

Feeling: ☐ **Fantastic**   ☐ **Good**   ☐ **Difficult**   ☐ **Very Difficult**

Weather   Temperature: _____ ° ___   Workout Gear: _____

Notes:

Saturday

Date: _____   **Week 6**

Vitals: **Resting HR:** _____ bpm   **Weight:** _____ kg/lbs   Hours Slept: _____ hrs

Sport: _____   Workout: _____

Course: _____   Duration: _____   Distance: _____

Intensity: ☐ **Maximum**   ☐ **Hard**   ☐ **Medium**   ☐ **Minimum**

Average HR: _____ bpm   Target HR: _____ bpm

Feeling: ☐ **Fantastic**   ☐ **Good**   ☐ **Difficult**   ☐ **Very Difficult**

Weather   Temperature: _____ ° ___   Workout Gear: _____

Notes:

_____

_____

Weekly Summary

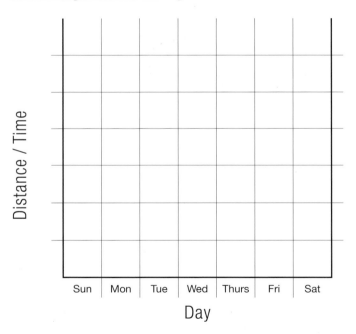

Total Time: _____   Total Distance: _____

Additional Information:

_____

_____

_____

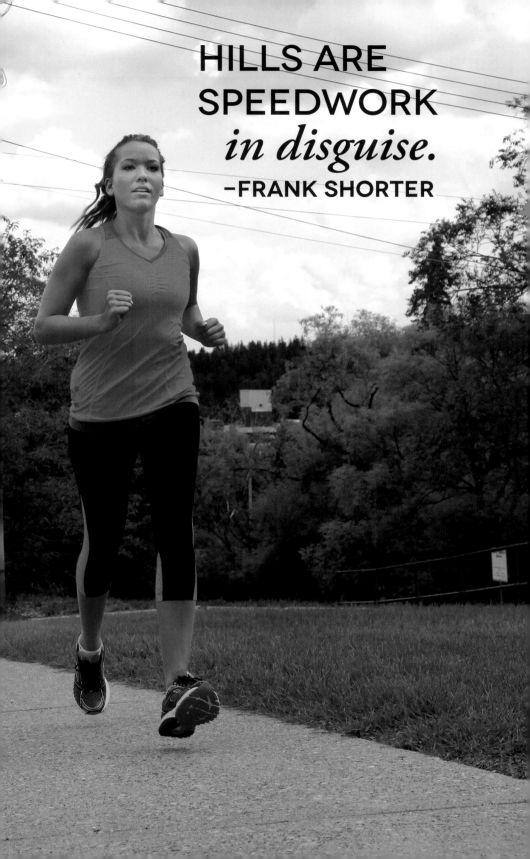

HILLS ARE
SPEEDWORK
in disguise.
−FRANK SHORTER

Sunday

Date: _____ **Week 7**

Vitals: **Resting HR:** _____ bpm **Weight:** _____ kg/lbs Hours Slept: _____ hrs

Sport: _____ Workout: _____

Course: _____ Duration: _____ Distance: _____

Intensity: ☐ **Maximum** ☐ **Hard** ☐ **Medium** ☐ **Minimum**

Average HR: _____ bpm Target HR: _____ bpm

Feeling: ☐ **Fantastic** ☐ **Good** ☐ **Difficult** ☐ **Very Difficult**

Weather Temperature: _____ ° ___ Workout Gear: _____

Notes:

_____

_____

Monday

Date: _____ **Week 7**

Vitals: **Resting HR:** _____ bpm **Weight:** _____ kg/lbs Hours Slept: _____ hrs

Sport: _____ Workout: _____

Course: _____ Duration: _____ Distance: _____

Intensity: ☐ **Maximum** ☐ **Hard** ☐ **Medium** ☐ **Minimum**

Average HR: _____ bpm Target HR: _____ bpm

Feeling: ☐ **Fantastic** ☐ **Good** ☐ **Difficult** ☐ **Very Difficult**

Weather Temperature: _____ ° ___ Workout Gear: _____

Notes:

_____

_____

Tuesday

Date: _____ **Week 7**

Vitals: **Resting HR:** _____ bpm **Weight:** _____ kg/lbs Hours Slept: _____ hrs

Sport: _____ Workout: _____

Course: _____ Duration: _____ Distance: _____

Intensity: ☐ **Maximum** ☐ **Hard** ☐ **Medium** ☐ **Minimum**

Average HR: _____ bpm Target HR: _____ bpm

Feeling: ☐ **Fantastic** ☐ **Good** ☐ **Difficult** ☐ **Very Difficult**

Weather Temperature: _____ ° ___ Workout Gear: _____

Notes:

_____

_____

Wednesday

Vitals: **Resting HR**: _____ bpm **Weight**: _____ kg/lbs Hours Slept: _____ hrs

Sport: _____ Workout: _____

Course: _____ Duration: _____ Distance: _____

Intensity: ☐ **Maximum** ☐ **Hard** ☐ **Medium** ☐ **Minimum**

Average HR: _____ bpm Target HR: _____ bpm

Feeling: ☐ **Fantastic** ☐ **Good** ☐ **Difficult** ☐ **Very Difficult**

Weather Temperature: _____ ° ___ Workout Gear: _____

Notes:

Thursday

Vitals: **Resting HR**: _____ bpm **Weight**: _____ kg/lbs Hours Slept: _____ hrs

Sport: _____ Workout: _____

Course: _____ Duration: _____ Distance: _____

Intensity: ☐ **Maximum** ☐ **Hard** ☐ **Medium** ☐ **Minimum**

Average HR: _____ bpm Target HR: _____ bpm

Feeling: ☐ **Fantastic** ☐ **Good** ☐ **Difficult** ☐ **Very Difficult**

Weather Temperature: _____ ° ___ Workout Gear: _____

Notes:

Friday

Vitals: **Resting HR**: _____ bpm **Weight**: _____ kg/lbs Hours Slept: _____ hrs

Sport: _____ Workout: _____

Course: _____ Duration: _____ Distance: _____

Intensity: ☐ **Maximum** ☐ **Hard** ☐ **Medium** ☐ **Minimum**

Average HR: _____ bpm Target HR: _____ bpm

Feeling: ☐ **Fantastic** ☐ **Good** ☐ **Difficult** ☐ **Very Difficult**

Weather Temperature: _____ ° ___ Workout Gear: _____

Notes:

Saturday

Vitals: **Resting HR**: _____ bpm   **Weight**: _____ kg/lbs   Hours Slept: _____ hrs

Sport: _____   Workout: _____

Course: _____   Duration: _____   Distance: _____

Intensity: ☐ **Maximum**   ☐ **Hard**   ☐ **Medium**   ☐ **Minimum**

Average HR: _____ bpm   Target HR: _____ bpm

Feeling: ☐ **Fantastic**   ☐ **Good**   ☐ **Difficult**   ☐ **Very Difficult**

Weather   Temperature: _____ ° ___   Workout Gear: _____

Notes: _____

_____

_____

Weekly Summary

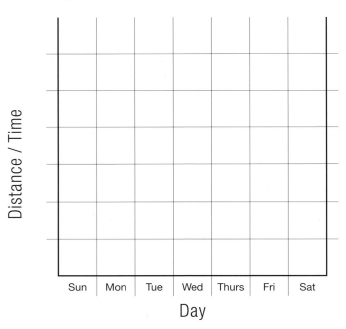

Total Time: _____   Total Distance: _____

Additional Information: _____

_____

_____

_____

Running is not a single event.

It's a lifestyle and a statement of who you are.

- John Stanton

Sunday

Vitals: **Resting HR**: _____ bpm   **Weight**: _____ kg/lbs   Hours Slept: _____ hrs

Sport: _____   Workout: _____

Course: _____   Duration: _____   Distance: _____

Intensity: ☐ **Maximum**   ☐ **Hard**   ☐ **Medium**   ☐ **Minimum**

Average HR: _____ bpm   Target HR: _____ bpm

Feeling: ☐ **Fantastic**   ☐ **Good**   ☐ **Difficult**   ☐ **Very Difficult**

Weather   Temperature: _____ ° ___   Workout Gear: _____

Notes:

Monday

Vitals: **Resting HR**: _____ bpm   **Weight**: _____ kg/lbs   Hours Slept: _____ hrs

Sport: _____   Workout: _____

Course: _____   Duration: _____   Distance: _____

Intensity: ☐ **Maximum**   ☐ **Hard**   ☐ **Medium**   ☐ **Minimum**

Average HR: _____ bpm   Target HR: _____ bpm

Feeling: ☐ **Fantastic**   ☐ **Good**   ☐ **Difficult**   ☐ **Very Difficult**

Weather   Temperature: _____ ° ___   Workout Gear: _____

Notes:

Tuesday

Vitals: **Resting HR**: _____ bpm   **Weight**: _____ kg/lbs   Hours Slept: _____ hrs

Sport: _____   Workout: _____

Course: _____   Duration: _____   Distance: _____

Intensity: ☐ **Maximum**   ☐ **Hard**   ☐ **Medium**   ☐ **Minimum**

Average HR: _____ bpm   Target HR: _____ bpm

Feeling: ☐ **Fantastic**   ☐ **Good**   ☐ **Difficult**   ☐ **Very Difficult**

Weather   Temperature: _____ ° ___   Workout Gear: _____

Notes:

Wednesday

Date: _____ **Week 8**

Vitals: **Resting HR**: _____ bpm **Weight**: _____ kg/lbs Hours Slept: _____ hrs

Sport: _____ Workout: _____

Course: _____ Duration: _____ Distance: _____

Intensity: ☐ **Maximum** ☐ **Hard** ☐ **Medium** ☐ **Minimum**

Average HR: _____ bpm Target HR: _____ bpm

Feeling: ☐ **Fantastic** ☐ **Good** ☐ **Difficult** ☐ **Very Difficult**

Weather Temperature: _____ ° ___ Workout Gear: _____

Notes: _____

_____

Thursday

Date: _____ **Week 8**

Vitals: **Resting HR**: _____ bpm **Weight**: _____ kg/lbs Hours Slept: _____ hrs

Sport: _____ Workout: _____

Course: _____ Duration: _____ Distance: _____

Intensity: ☐ **Maximum** ☐ **Hard** ☐ **Medium** ☐ **Minimum**

Average HR: _____ bpm Target HR: _____ bpm

Feeling: ☐ **Fantastic** ☐ **Good** ☐ **Difficult** ☐ **Very Difficult**

Weather Temperature: _____ ° ___ Workout Gear: _____

Notes: _____

_____

Friday

Date: _____ **Week 8**

Vitals: **Resting HR**: _____ bpm **Weight**: _____ kg/lbs Hours Slept: _____ hrs

Sport: _____ Workout: _____

Course: _____ Duration: _____ Distance: _____

Intensity: ☐ **Maximum** ☐ **Hard** ☐ **Medium** ☐ **Minimum**

Average HR: _____ bpm Target HR: _____ bpm

Feeling: ☐ **Fantastic** ☐ **Good** ☐ **Difficult** ☐ **Very Difficult**

Weather Temperature: _____ ° ___ Workout Gear: _____

Notes: _____

_____

Saturday

Date: _____   **Week 8**

Vitals: **Resting HR:** _____ bpm   **Weight:** _____ kg/lbs   Hours Slept: _____ hrs

Sport: _____   Workout: _____

Course: _____   Duration: _____   Distance: _____

Intensity: □ **Maximum**   □ **Hard**   □ **Medium**   □ **Minimum**

Average HR: _____ bpm   Target HR: _____ bpm

Feeling: □ **Fantastic**   □ **Good**   □ **Difficult**   □ **Very Difficult**

Weather   Temperature: _____ ° ___   Workout Gear: _____

Notes:
_____
_____

Weekly Summary

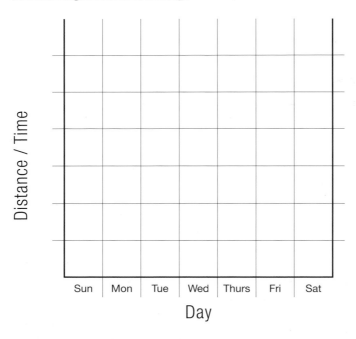

Total Time: _____   Total Distance: _____

Additional Information:
_____
_____
_____
_____

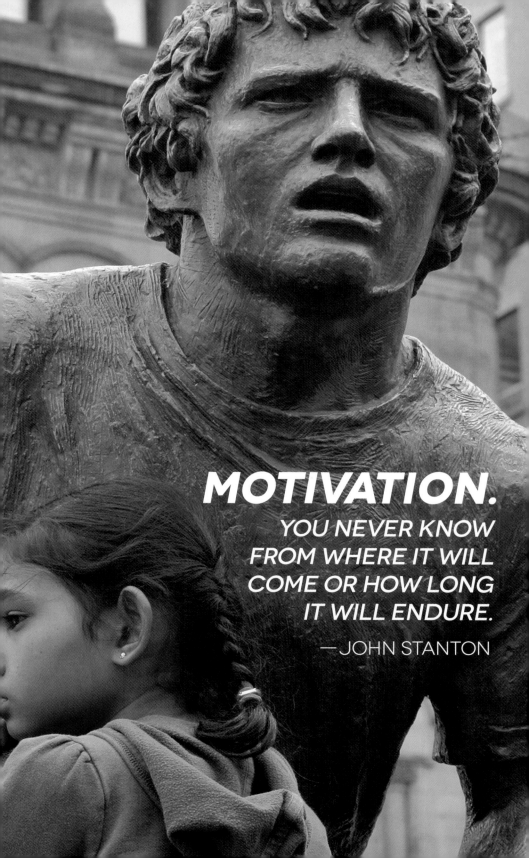

MOTIVATION.
*YOU NEVER KNOW
FROM WHERE IT WILL
COME OR HOW LONG
IT WILL ENDURE.*

—JOHN STANTON

Sunday

Vitals: **Resting HR:** _____ bpm **Weight:** _____ kg/lbs Hours Slept: _____ hrs

Sport: _____ Workout: _____

Course: _____ Duration: _____ Distance: _____

Intensity: ☐ **Maximum** ☐ **Hard** ☐ **Medium** ☐ **Minimum**

Average HR: _____ bpm Target HR: _____ bpm

Feeling: ☐ **Fantastic** ☐ **Good** ☐ **Difficult** ☐ **Very Difficult**

Weather Temperature: _____ ° ___ Workout Gear: _____

Notes:

_____

_____

Monday

Vitals: **Resting HR:** _____ bpm **Weight:** _____ kg/lbs Hours Slept: _____ hrs

Sport: _____ Workout: _____

Course: _____ Duration: _____ Distance: _____

Intensity: ☐ **Maximum** ☐ **Hard** ☐ **Medium** ☐ **Minimum**

Average HR: _____ bpm Target HR: _____ bpm

Feeling: ☐ **Fantastic** ☐ **Good** ☐ **Difficult** ☐ **Very Difficult**

Weather Temperature: _____ ° ___ Workout Gear: _____

Notes:

_____

_____

Tuesday

Vitals: **Resting HR:** _____ bpm **Weight:** _____ kg/lbs Hours Slept: _____ hrs

Sport: _____ Workout: _____

Course: _____ Duration: _____ Distance: _____

Intensity: ☐ **Maximum** ☐ **Hard** ☐ **Medium** ☐ **Minimum**

Average HR: _____ bpm Target HR: _____ bpm

Feeling: ☐ **Fantastic** ☐ **Good** ☐ **Difficult** ☐ **Very Difficult**

Weather Temperature: _____ ° ___ Workout Gear: _____

Notes:

_____

_____

Wednesday

Date: _____   **Week 9**

Vitals: **Resting HR:** _____ bpm   **Weight:** _____ kg/lbs   Hours Slept: _____ hrs

Sport: _____   Workout: _____

Course: _____   Duration: _____   Distance: _____

Intensity: ☐ **Maximum**   ☐ **Hard**   ☐ **Medium**   ☐ **Minimum**

Average HR: _____ bpm   Target HR: _____ bpm

Feeling: ☐ **Fantastic**   ☐ **Good**   ☐ **Difficult**   ☐ **Very Difficult**

Weather   Temperature: _____ ° __   Workout Gear: _____

Notes: _____

_____

_____

Thursday

Date: _____   **Week 9**

Vitals: **Resting HR:** _____ bpm   **Weight:** _____ kg/lbs   Hours Slept: _____ hrs

Sport: _____   Workout: _____

Course: _____   Duration: _____   Distance: _____

Intensity: ☐ **Maximum**   ☐ **Hard**   ☐ **Medium**   ☐ **Minimum**

Average HR: _____ bpm   Target HR: _____ bpm

Feeling: ☐ **Fantastic**   ☐ **Good**   ☐ **Difficult**   ☐ **Very Difficult**

Weather   Temperature: _____ ° __   Workout Gear: _____

Notes: _____

_____

_____

Friday

Date: _____   **Week 9**

Vitals: **Resting HR:** _____ bpm   **Weight:** _____ kg/lbs   Hours Slept: _____ hrs

Sport: _____   Workout: _____

Course: _____   Duration: _____   Distance: _____

Intensity: ☐ **Maximum**   ☐ **Hard**   ☐ **Medium**   ☐ **Minimum**

Average HR: _____ bpm   Target HR: _____ bpm

Feeling: ☐ **Fantastic**   ☐ **Good**   ☐ **Difficult**   ☐ **Very Difficult**

Weather   Temperature: _____ ° __   Workout Gear: _____

Notes: _____

_____

_____

Saturday

Vitals: **Resting HR:** _____ bpm **Weight:** _____ kg/lbs Hours Slept: _____ hrs

Sport: _____ Workout: _____

Course: _____ Duration: _____ Distance: _____

Intensity: ☐ **Maximum** ☐ **Hard** ☐ **Medium** ☐ **Minimum**

Average HR: _____ bpm Target HR: _____ bpm

Feeling: ☐ **Fantastic** ☐ **Good** ☐ **Difficult** ☐ **Very Difficult**

Weather Temperature: _____ ° ___ Workout Gear: _____

Notes: _____

_____

_____

Weekly Summary

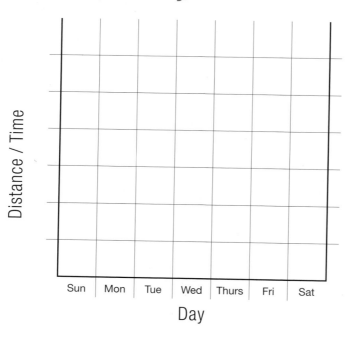

Total Time: _____ Total Distance: _____

Additional Information: _____

_____

_____

_____

_____

You have to forget your last marathon before you try another.

Your mind can't know what's coming.

- Frank Shorter

Sunday

Date: _____   **Week 10**

Vitals: **Resting HR:** _____ bpm   **Weight:** _____ kg/lbs   Hours Slept: _____ hrs

Sport: _____   Workout: _____

Course: _____   Duration: _____   Distance: _____

Intensity: ☐ **Maximum**   ☐ **Hard**   ☐ **Medium**   ☐ **Minimum**

Average HR: _____ bpm   Target HR: _____ bpm

Feeling: ☐ **Fantastic**   ☐ **Good**   ☐ **Difficult**   ☐ **Very Difficult**

Weather   Temperature: _____ ° ___   Workout Gear: _____

Notes: _____

_____

Monday

Date: _____   **Week 10**

Vitals: **Resting HR:** _____ bpm   **Weight:** _____ kg/lbs   Hours Slept: _____ hrs

Sport: _____   Workout: _____

Course: _____   Duration: _____   Distance: _____

Intensity: ☐ **Maximum**   ☐ **Hard**   ☐ **Medium**   ☐ **Minimum**

Average HR: _____ bpm   Target HR: _____ bpm

Feeling: ☐ **Fantastic**   ☐ **Good**   ☐ **Difficult**   ☐ **Very Difficult**

Weather   Temperature: _____ ° ___   Workout Gear: _____

Notes: _____

_____

Tuesday

Date: _____   **Week 10**

Vitals: **Resting HR:** _____ bpm   **Weight:** _____ kg/lbs   Hours Slept: _____ hrs

Sport: _____   Workout: _____

Course: _____   Duration: _____   Distance: _____

Intensity: ☐ **Maximum**   ☐ **Hard**   ☐ **Medium**   ☐ **Minimum**

Average HR: _____ bpm   Target HR: _____ bpm

Feeling: ☐ **Fantastic**   ☐ **Good**   ☐ **Difficult**   ☐ **Very Difficult**

Weather   Temperature: _____ ° ___   Workout Gear: _____

Notes: _____

_____

Wednesday

Date: _____ **Week 10**

Vitals: **Resting HR:** _____ bpm   **Weight:** _____ kg/lbs   Hours Slept: _____ hrs

Sport: _____   Workout: _____

Course: _____   Duration: _____   Distance: _____

Intensity: ☐ **Maximum**   ☐ **Hard**   ☐ **Medium**   ☐ **Minimum**

Average HR: _____ bpm   Target HR: _____ bpm

Feeling: ☐ **Fantastic**   ☐ **Good**   ☐ **Difficult**   ☐ **Very Difficult**

Weather   Temperature: _____ ° ___   Workout Gear: _____

Notes:

_____
_____

Thursday

Date: _____ **Week 10**

Vitals: **Resting HR:** _____ bpm   **Weight:** _____ kg/lbs   Hours Slept: _____ hrs

Sport: _____   Workout: _____

Course: _____   Duration: _____   Distance: _____

Intensity: ☐ **Maximum**   ☐ **Hard**   ☐ **Medium**   ☐ **Minimum**

Average HR: _____ bpm   Target HR: _____ bpm

Feeling: ☐ **Fantastic**   ☐ **Good**   ☐ **Difficult**   ☐ **Very Difficult**

Weather   Temperature: _____ ° ___   Workout Gear: _____

Notes:

_____
_____

Friday

Date: _____ **Week 10**

Vitals: **Resting HR:** _____ bpm   **Weight:** _____ kg/lbs   Hours Slept: _____ hrs

Sport: _____   Workout: _____

Course: _____   Duration: _____   Distance: _____

Intensity: ☐ **Maximum**   ☐ **Hard**   ☐ **Medium**   ☐ **Minimum**

Average HR: _____ bpm   Target HR: _____ bpm

Feeling: ☐ **Fantastic**   ☐ **Good**   ☐ **Difficult**   ☐ **Very Difficult**

Weather   Temperature: _____ ° ___   Workout Gear: _____

Notes:

_____
_____

Saturday

Date: _____ **Week 10**

Vitals: **Resting HR**: _____ bpm **Weight**: _____ kg/lbs Hours Slept: _____ hrs

Sport: _____ Workout: _____

Course: _____ Duration: _____ Distance: _____

Intensity: ☐ **Maximum** ☐ **Hard** ☐ **Medium** ☐ **Minimum**

Average HR: _____ bpm Target HR: _____ bpm

Feeling: ☐ **Fantastic** ☐ **Good** ☐ **Difficult** ☐ **Very Difficult**

Weather Temperature: _____ ° ___ Workout Gear: _____

Notes: _____

_____

Weekly Summary

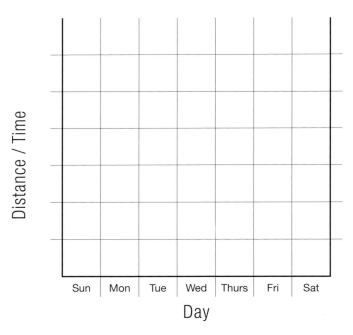

Total Time: _____ Total Distance: _____

Additional Information: _____

_____

_____

_____

**MOST MISTAKES IN A RACE
ARE MADE IN THE FIRST
TWO MINUTES; PERHAPS IN
THE VERY** *first* **MINUTE.**

- JACK DANIELS
**EXERCISE PHYSIOLOGIST
AND COACH**

Sunday

Date: _____   **Week 11**

Vitals: **Resting HR:** _____ bpm   **Weight:** _____ kg/lbs   Hours Slept: _____ hrs

Sport: _____   Workout: _____

Course: _____   Duration: _____   Distance: _____

Intensity: ☐ **Maximum**   ☐ **Hard**   ☐ **Medium**   ☐ **Minimum**

Average HR: _____ bpm   Target HR: _____ bpm

Feeling: ☐ **Fantastic**   ☐ **Good**   ☐ **Difficult**   ☐ **Very Difficult**

Weather   Temperature: _____ ° ___   Workout Gear: _____

Notes: _____

_____

Monday

Date: _____   **Week 11**

Vitals: **Resting HR:** _____ bpm   **Weight:** _____ kg/lbs   Hours Slept: _____ hrs

Sport: _____   Workout: _____

Course: _____   Duration: _____   Distance: _____

Intensity: ☐ **Maximum**   ☐ **Hard**   ☐ **Medium**   ☐ **Minimum**

Average HR: _____ bpm   Target HR: _____ bpm

Feeling: ☐ **Fantastic**   ☐ **Good**   ☐ **Difficult**   ☐ **Very Difficult**

Weather   Temperature: _____ ° ___   Workout Gear: _____

Notes: _____

_____

Tuesday

Date: _____   **Week 11**

Vitals: **Resting HR:** _____ bpm   **Weight:** _____ kg/lbs   Hours Slept: _____ hrs

Sport: _____   Workout: _____

Course: _____   Duration: _____   Distance: _____

Intensity: ☐ **Maximum**   ☐ **Hard**   ☐ **Medium**   ☐ **Minimum**

Average HR: _____ bpm   Target HR: _____ bpm

Feeling: ☐ **Fantastic**   ☐ **Good**   ☐ **Difficult**   ☐ **Very Difficult**

Weather   Temperature: _____ ° ___   Workout Gear: _____

Notes: _____

_____

Wednesday

Vitals: **Resting HR:** _____ bpm   **Weight:** _____ kg/lbs   Hours Slept: _____ hrs

Sport: _____   Workout: _____

Course: _____   Duration: _____   Distance: _____

Intensity: ☐ **Maximum**   ☐ **Hard**   ☐ **Medium**   ☐ **Minimum**

Average HR: _____ bpm   Target HR: _____ bpm

Feeling: ☐ **Fantastic**   ☐ **Good**   ☐ **Difficult**   ☐ **Very Difficult**

Weather   Temperature: _____ ° ___   Workout Gear: _____

Notes:
_____

_____

Thursday

Vitals: **Resting HR:** _____ bpm   **Weight:** _____ kg/lbs   Hours Slept: _____ hrs

Sport: _____   Workout: _____

Course: _____   Duration: _____   Distance: _____

Intensity: ☐ **Maximum**   ☐ **Hard**   ☐ **Medium**   ☐ **Minimum**

Average HR: _____ bpm   Target HR: _____ bpm

Feeling: ☐ **Fantastic**   ☐ **Good**   ☐ **Difficult**   ☐ **Very Difficult**

Weather   Temperature: _____ ° ___   Workout Gear: _____

Notes:
_____

_____

Friday

Vitals: **Resting HR:** _____ bpm   **Weight:** _____ kg/lbs   Hours Slept: _____ hrs

Sport: _____   Workout: _____

Course: _____   Duration: _____   Distance: _____

Intensity: ☐ **Maximum**   ☐ **Hard**   ☐ **Medium**   ☐ **Minimum**

Average HR: _____ bpm   Target HR: _____ bpm

Feeling: ☐ **Fantastic**   ☐ **Good**   ☐ **Difficult**   ☐ **Very Difficult**

Weather   Temperature: _____ ° ___   Workout Gear: _____

Notes:
_____

_____

Saturday

Date: _____   Week 11

Vitals: **Resting HR:** _____ bpm   **Weight:** _____ kg/lbs   Hours Slept: _____ hrs

Sport: _____   Workout: _____

Course: _____   Duration: _____   Distance: _____

Intensity: ☐ **Maximum**   ☐ **Hard**   ☐ **Medium**   ☐ **Minimum**

Average HR: _____ bpm   Target HR: _____ bpm

Feeling: ☐ **Fantastic**   ☐ **Good**   ☐ **Difficult**   ☐ **Very Difficult**

Weather   Temperature: _____ ° ___   Workout Gear: _____

Notes: _____

_____

_____

Weekly Summary

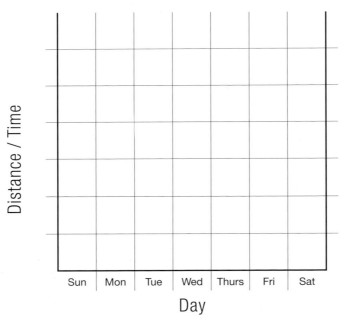

Total Time: _____   Total Distance: _____

Additional Information: _____

_____

_____

_____

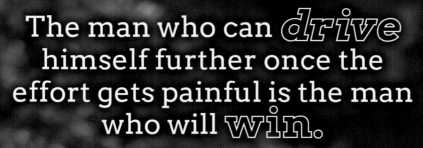

The man who can *drive* himself further once the effort gets painful is the man who will **win.**

— *Roger Bannister*
First 4-minute miler

Sunday

Vitals: **Resting HR:** _____ bpm   **Weight:** _____ kg/lbs   Hours Slept: _____ hrs

Sport: _____   Workout: _____

Course: _____   Duration: _____   Distance: _____

Intensity: ☐ **Maximum**   ☐ **Hard**   ☐ **Medium**   ☐ **Minimum**

Average HR: _____ bpm   Target HR: _____ bpm

Feeling: ☐ **Fantastic**   ☐ **Good**   ☐ **Difficult**   ☐ **Very Difficult**

Weather   Temperature: _____ ° ___   Workout Gear: _____

Notes:

_____

_____

Monday

Vitals: **Resting HR:** _____ bpm   **Weight:** _____ kg/lbs   Hours Slept: _____ hrs

Sport: _____   Workout: _____

Course: _____   Duration: _____   Distance: _____

Intensity: ☐ **Maximum**   ☐ **Hard**   ☐ **Medium**   ☐ **Minimum**

Average HR: _____ bpm   Target HR: _____ bpm

Feeling: ☐ **Fantastic**   ☐ **Good**   ☐ **Difficult**   ☐ **Very Difficult**

Weather   Temperature: _____ ° ___   Workout Gear: _____

Notes:

_____

_____

Tuesday

Vitals: **Resting HR:** _____ bpm   **Weight:** _____ kg/lbs   Hours Slept: _____ hrs

Sport: _____   Workout: _____

Course: _____   Duration: _____   Distance: _____

Intensity: ☐ **Maximum**   ☐ **Hard**   ☐ **Medium**   ☐ **Minimum**

Average HR: _____ bpm   Target HR: _____ bpm

Feeling: ☐ **Fantastic**   ☐ **Good**   ☐ **Difficult**   ☐ **Very Difficult**

Weather   Temperature: _____ ° ___   Workout Gear: _____

Notes:

_____

_____

Wednesday

Vitals: **Resting HR:** _____ bpm   **Weight:** _____ kg/lbs   Hours Slept: _____ hrs

Sport: _____   Workout: _____

Course: _____   Duration: _____   Distance: _____

Intensity: ☐ **Maximum**   ☐ **Hard**   ☐ **Medium**   ☐ **Minimum**

Average HR: _____ bpm   Target HR: _____ bpm

Feeling: ☐ **Fantastic**   ☐ **Good**   ☐ **Difficult**   ☐ **Very Difficult**

Weather   Temperature: _____ ° ___   Workout Gear: _____

Notes: _____

_____

Thursday

Vitals: **Resting HR:** _____ bpm   **Weight:** _____ kg/lbs   Hours Slept: _____ hrs

Sport: _____   Workout: _____

Course: _____   Duration: _____   Distance: _____

Intensity: ☐ **Maximum**   ☐ **Hard**   ☐ **Medium**   ☐ **Minimum**

Average HR: _____ bpm   Target HR: _____ bpm

Feeling: ☐ **Fantastic**   ☐ **Good**   ☐ **Difficult**   ☐ **Very Difficult**

Weather   Temperature: _____ ° ___   Workout Gear: _____

Notes: _____

_____

Friday

Vitals: **Resting HR:** _____ bpm   **Weight:** _____ kg/lbs   Hours Slept: _____ hrs

Sport: _____   Workout: _____

Course: _____   Duration: _____   Distance: _____

Intensity: ☐ **Maximum**   ☐ **Hard**   ☐ **Medium**   ☐ **Minimum**

Average HR: _____ bpm   Target HR: _____ bpm

Feeling: ☐ **Fantastic**   ☐ **Good**   ☐ **Difficult**   ☐ **Very Difficult**

Weather   Temperature: _____ ° ___   Workout Gear: _____

Notes: _____

_____

Saturday

Date: _____   Week 12

Vitals: **Resting HR**: _____ bpm   **Weight**: _____ kg/lbs   Hours Slept: _____ hrs

Sport: _____   Workout: _____

Course: _____   Duration: _____   Distance: _____

Intensity: ☐ **Maximum**   ☐ **Hard**   ☐ **Medium**   ☐ **Minimum**

Average HR: _____ bpm   Target HR: _____ bpm

Feeling: ☐ **Fantastic**   ☐ **Good**   ☐ **Difficult**   ☐ **Very Difficult**

Weather   Temperature: _____ ° ___   Workout Gear: _____

Notes: _____

_____

Weekly Summary

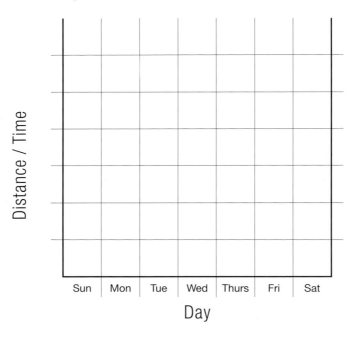

Total Time: _____   Total Distance: _____

Additional Information: _____

_____

_____

_____

THE WILL TO WIN
MEANS NOTHING IF YOU
HAVEN'T THE WILL TO
prepare.

– JUMA IKANGAA
1989 NYC MARATHON WINNER

Sunday

Vitals: **Resting HR**: _____ bpm   **Weight**: _____ kg/lbs   Hours Slept: _____ hrs

Sport: _____   Workout: _____

Course: _____   Duration: _____   Distance: _____

Intensity: ☐ **Maximum**   ☐ **Hard**   ☐ **Medium**   ☐ **Minimum**

Average HR: _____ bpm   Target HR: _____ bpm

Feeling: ☐ **Fantastic**   ☐ **Good**   ☐ **Difficult**   ☐ **Very Difficult**

Weather   Temperature: _____ ° ___   Workout Gear: _____

Notes:

Monday

Vitals: **Resting HR**: _____ bpm   **Weight**: _____ kg/lbs   Hours Slept: _____ hrs

Sport: _____   Workout: _____

Course: _____   Duration: _____   Distance: _____

Intensity: ☐ **Maximum**   ☐ **Hard**   ☐ **Medium**   ☐ **Minimum**

Average HR: _____ bpm   Target HR: _____ bpm

Feeling: ☐ **Fantastic**   ☐ **Good**   ☐ **Difficult**   ☐ **Very Difficult**

Weather   Temperature: _____ ° ___   Workout Gear: _____

Notes:

Tuesday

Vitals: **Resting HR**: _____ bpm   **Weight**: _____ kg/lbs   Hours Slept: _____ hrs

Sport: _____   Workout: _____

Course: _____   Duration: _____   Distance: _____

Intensity: ☐ **Maximum**   ☐ **Hard**   ☐ **Medium**   ☐ **Minimum**

Average HR: _____ bpm   Target HR: _____ bpm

Feeling: ☐ **Fantastic**   ☐ **Good**   ☐ **Difficult**   ☐ **Very Difficult**

Weather   Temperature: _____ ° ___   Workout Gear: _____

Notes:

Wednesday

Date: _____   **Week 13**

Vitals: **Resting HR:** _____ bpm   **Weight:** _____ kg/lbs   Hours Slept: _____ hrs

Sport: _____   Workout: _____

Course: _____   Duration: _____   Distance: _____

Intensity: ☐ **Maximum**   ☐ **Hard**   ☐ **Medium**   ☐ **Minimum**

Average HR: _____ bpm   Target HR: _____ bpm

Feeling: ☐ **Fantastic**   ☐ **Good**   ☐ **Difficult**   ☐ **Very Difficult**

Weather   Temperature: _____ ° __   Workout Gear: _____

Notes:

Thursday

Date: _____   **Week 13**

Vitals: **Resting HR:** _____ bpm   **Weight:** _____ kg/lbs   Hours Slept: _____ hrs

Sport: _____   Workout: _____

Course: _____   Duration: _____   Distance: _____

Intensity: ☐ **Maximum**   ☐ **Hard**   ☐ **Medium**   ☐ **Minimum**

Average HR: _____ bpm   Target HR: _____ bpm

Feeling: ☐ **Fantastic**   ☐ **Good**   ☐ **Difficult**   ☐ **Very Difficult**

Weather   Temperature: _____ ° __   Workout Gear: _____

Notes:

Friday

Date: _____   **Week 13**

Vitals: **Resting HR:** _____ bpm   **Weight:** _____ kg/lbs   Hours Slept: _____ hrs

Sport: _____   Workout: _____

Course: _____   Duration: _____   Distance: _____

Intensity: ☐ **Maximum**   ☐ **Hard**   ☐ **Medium**   ☐ **Minimum**

Average HR: _____ bpm   Target HR: _____ bpm

Feeling: ☐ **Fantastic**   ☐ **Good**   ☐ **Difficult**   ☐ **Very Difficult**

Weather   Temperature: _____ ° __   Workout Gear: _____

Notes:

Saturday

Vitals: **Resting HR:** _____ bpm   **Weight:** _____ kg/lbs   Hours Slept: _____ hrs

Sport: _____   Workout: _____

Course: _____   Duration: _____   Distance: _____

Intensity: ☐ **Maximum**   ☐ **Hard**   ☐ **Medium**   ☐ **Minimum**

Average HR: _____ bpm   Target HR: _____ bpm

Feeling: ☐ **Fantastic**   ☐ **Good**   ☐ **Difficult**   ☐ **Very Difficult**

Weather   Temperature: _____ ° ___   Workout Gear: _____

Notes: _____

_____

Weekly Summary

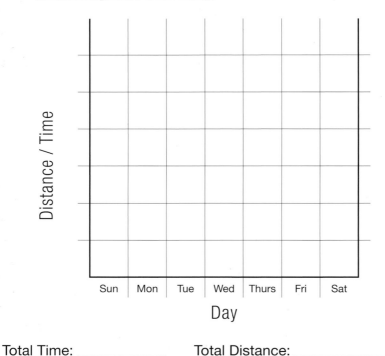

Total Time: _____   Total Distance: _____

Additional Information: _____

_____

_____

_____

A healthy body is a *guest-chamber* for the soul.

– Francis Bacon

Sunday

Vitals: **Resting HR:** _____ bpm   **Weight:** _____ kg/lbs   Hours Slept: _____ hrs

Sport: _____   Workout: _____

Course: _____   Duration: _____   Distance: _____

Intensity: ☐ **Maximum**   ☐ **Hard**   ☐ **Medium**   ☐ **Minimum**

Average HR: _____ bpm   Target HR: _____ bpm

Feeling: ☐ **Fantastic**   ☐ **Good**   ☐ **Difficult**   ☐ **Very Difficult**

Weather   Temperature: _____ ° ___   Workout Gear: _____

Notes:

Monday

Vitals: **Resting HR:** _____ bpm   **Weight:** _____ kg/lbs   Hours Slept: _____ hrs

Sport: _____   Workout: _____

Course: _____   Duration: _____   Distance: _____

Intensity: ☐ **Maximum**   ☐ **Hard**   ☐ **Medium**   ☐ **Minimum**

Average HR: _____ bpm   Target HR: _____ bpm

Feeling: ☐ **Fantastic**   ☐ **Good**   ☐ **Difficult**   ☐ **Very Difficult**

Weather   Temperature: _____ ° ___   Workout Gear: _____

Notes:

Tuesday

Vitals: **Resting HR:** _____ bpm   **Weight:** _____ kg/lbs   Hours Slept: _____ hrs

Sport: _____   Workout: _____

Course: _____   Duration: _____   Distance: _____

Intensity: ☐ **Maximum**   ☐ **Hard**   ☐ **Medium**   ☐ **Minimum**

Average HR: _____ bpm   Target HR: _____ bpm

Feeling: ☐ **Fantastic**   ☐ **Good**   ☐ **Difficult**   ☐ **Very Difficult**

Weather   Temperature: _____ ° ___   Workout Gear: _____

Notes:

Wednesday
Date: **Week 14**

Vitals: **Resting HR**: _____ bpm   **Weight**: _____ kg/lbs   Hours Slept: _____ hrs

Sport: _____   Workout: _____

Course: _____   Duration: _____   Distance: _____

Intensity: ☐ **Maximum**   ☐ **Hard**   ☐ **Medium**   ☐ **Minimum**

Average HR: _____ bpm   Target HR: _____ bpm

Feeling: ☐ **Fantastic**   ☐ **Good**   ☐ **Difficult**   ☐ **Very Difficult**

Weather   Temperature: _____ ° ___   Workout Gear: _____

Notes:

Thursday
Date: **Week 14**

Vitals: **Resting HR**: _____ bpm   **Weight**: _____ kg/lbs   Hours Slept: _____ hrs

Sport: _____   Workout: _____

Course: _____   Duration: _____   Distance: _____

Intensity: ☐ **Maximum**   ☐ **Hard**   ☐ **Medium**   ☐ **Minimum**

Average HR: _____ bpm   Target HR: _____ bpm

Feeling: ☐ **Fantastic**   ☐ **Good**   ☐ **Difficult**   ☐ **Very Difficult**

Weather   Temperature: _____ ° ___   Workout Gear: _____

Notes:

Friday
Date: **Week 14**

Vitals: **Resting HR**: _____ bpm   **Weight**: _____ kg/lbs   Hours Slept: _____ hrs

Sport: _____   Workout: _____

Course: _____   Duration: _____   Distance: _____

Intensity: ☐ **Maximum**   ☐ **Hard**   ☐ **Medium**   ☐ **Minimum**

Average HR: _____ bpm   Target HR: _____ bpm

Feeling: ☐ **Fantastic**   ☐ **Good**   ☐ **Difficult**   ☐ **Very Difficult**

Weather   Temperature: _____ ° ___   Workout Gear: _____

Notes:

Saturday

Vitals: **Resting HR:** _____ bpm **Weight:** _____ kg/lbs Hours Slept: _____ hrs

Sport: _____ Workout: _____

Course: _____ Duration: _____ Distance: _____

Intensity: ☐ **Maximum** ☐ **Hard** ☐ **Medium** ☐ **Minimum**

Average HR: _____ bpm Target HR: _____ bpm

Feeling: ☐ **Fantastic** ☐ **Good** ☐ **Difficult** ☐ **Very Difficult**

Weather Temperature: _____ ° ___ Workout Gear: _____

Notes: _____

Weekly Summary

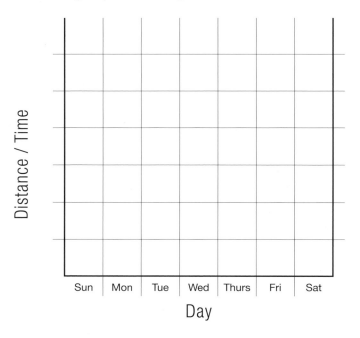

Total Time: _____ Total Distance: _____

Additional Information: _____

There are clubs you can't belong to, neighbourhoods you can't live in, schools you can't get into, but *the roads are always open.*

— Nike

Sunday

Date: _____ **Week 15**

Vitals: **Resting HR:** _____ bpm **Weight:** _____ kg/lbs Hours Slept: _____ hrs

Sport: _____ Workout: _____

Course: _____ Duration: _____ Distance: _____

Intensity: ☐ **Maximum** ☐ **Hard** ☐ **Medium** ☐ **Minimum**

Average HR: _____ bpm Target HR: _____ bpm

Feeling: ☐ **Fantastic** ☐ **Good** ☐ **Difficult** ☐ **Very Difficult**

Weather Temperature: _____ ° ____ Workout Gear: _____

Notes: _____

_____

Monday

Date: _____ **Week 15**

Vitals: **Resting HR:** _____ bpm **Weight:** _____ kg/lbs Hours Slept: _____ hrs

Sport: _____ Workout: _____

Course: _____ Duration: _____ Distance: _____

Intensity: ☐ **Maximum** ☐ **Hard** ☐ **Medium** ☐ **Minimum**

Average HR: _____ bpm Target HR: _____ bpm

Feeling: ☐ **Fantastic** ☐ **Good** ☐ **Difficult** ☐ **Very Difficult**

Weather Temperature: _____ ° ____ Workout Gear: _____

Notes: _____

_____

Tuesday

Date: _____ **Week 15**

Vitals: **Resting HR:** _____ bpm **Weight:** _____ kg/lbs Hours Slept: _____ hrs

Sport: _____ Workout: _____

Course: _____ Duration: _____ Distance: _____

Intensity: ☐ **Maximum** ☐ **Hard** ☐ **Medium** ☐ **Minimum**

Average HR: _____ bpm Target HR: _____ bpm

Feeling: ☐ **Fantastic** ☐ **Good** ☐ **Difficult** ☐ **Very Difficult**

Weather Temperature: _____ ° ____ Workout Gear: _____

Notes: _____

_____

Wednesday

Vitals: **Resting HR:** _____ bpm   **Weight:** _____ kg/lbs   Hours Slept: _____ hrs

Sport: _____   Workout: _____

Course: _____   Duration: _____   Distance: _____

Intensity: ☐ **Maximum**   ☐ **Hard**   ☐ **Medium**   ☐ **Minimum**

Average HR: _____ bpm   Target HR: _____ bpm

Feeling: ☐ **Fantastic**   ☐ **Good**   ☐ **Difficult**   ☐ **Very Difficult**

Weather   Temperature: _____ ° ___   Workout Gear: _____

Notes:

Thursday

Vitals: **Resting HR:** _____ bpm   **Weight:** _____ kg/lbs   Hours Slept: _____ hrs

Sport: _____   Workout: _____

Course: _____   Duration: _____   Distance: _____

Intensity: ☐ **Maximum**   ☐ **Hard**   ☐ **Medium**   ☐ **Minimum**

Average HR: _____ bpm   Target HR: _____ bpm

Feeling: ☐ **Fantastic**   ☐ **Good**   ☐ **Difficult**   ☐ **Very Difficult**

Weather   Temperature: _____ ° ___   Workout Gear: _____

Notes:

Friday

Vitals: **Resting HR:** _____ bpm   **Weight:** _____ kg/lbs   Hours Slept: _____ hrs

Sport: _____   Workout: _____

Course: _____   Duration: _____   Distance: _____

Intensity: ☐ **Maximum**   ☐ **Hard**   ☐ **Medium**   ☐ **Minimum**

Average HR: _____ bpm   Target HR: _____ bpm

Feeling: ☐ **Fantastic**   ☐ **Good**   ☐ **Difficult**   ☐ **Very Difficult**

Weather   Temperature: _____ ° ___   Workout Gear: _____

Notes:

Saturday

Date: _____   **Week 15**

Vitals: **Resting HR:** _____ bpm   **Weight:** _____ kg/lbs   Hours Slept: _____ hrs

Sport: _____   Workout: _____

Course: _____   Duration: _____   Distance: _____

Intensity: ☐ **Maximum**   ☐ **Hard**   ☐ **Medium**   ☐ **Minimum**

Average HR: _____ bpm   Target HR: _____ bpm

Feeling: ☐ **Fantastic**   ☐ **Good**   ☐ **Difficult**   ☐ **Very Difficult**

Weather   Temperature: _____ ° ___   Workout Gear: _____

Notes: _____

_____

Weekly Summary

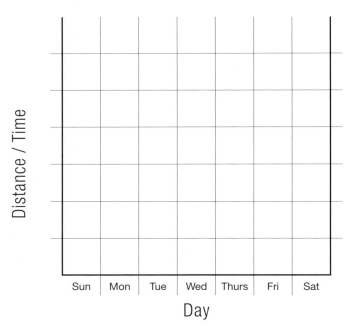

Total Time: _____   Total Distance: _____

Additional Information: _____

_____

_____

_____

Nothing is particularly hard
if you divide it into *small steps.*
— Henry Ford

Sunday

Date: _____   **Week 16**

Vitals: **Resting HR**: _____ bpm   **Weight**: _____ kg/lbs   Hours Slept: _____ hrs

Sport: _____   Workout: _____

Course: _____   Duration: _____   Distance: _____

Intensity: ☐ **Maximum**   ☐ **Hard**   ☐ **Medium**   ☐ **Minimum**

Average HR: _____ bpm   Target HR: _____ bpm

Feeling: ☐ **Fantastic**   ☐ **Good**   ☐ **Difficult**   ☐ **Very Difficult**

Weather   Temperature: _____ ° ___   Workout Gear: _____

Notes: _____

_____

Monday

Date: _____   **Week 16**

Vitals: **Resting HR**: _____ bpm   **Weight**: _____ kg/lbs   Hours Slept: _____ hrs

Sport: _____   Workout: _____

Course: _____   Duration: _____   Distance: _____

Intensity: ☐ **Maximum**   ☐ **Hard**   ☐ **Medium**   ☐ **Minimum**

Average HR: _____ bpm   Target HR: _____ bpm

Feeling: ☐ **Fantastic**   ☐ **Good**   ☐ **Difficult**   ☐ **Very Difficult**

Weather   Temperature: _____ ° ___   Workout Gear: _____

Notes: _____

_____

Tuesday

Date: _____   **Week 16**

Vitals: **Resting HR**: _____ bpm   **Weight**: _____ kg/lbs   Hours Slept: _____ hrs

Sport: _____   Workout: _____

Course: _____   Duration: _____   Distance: _____

Intensity: ☐ **Maximum**   ☐ **Hard**   ☐ **Medium**   ☐ **Minimum**

Average HR: _____ bpm   Target HR: _____ bpm

Feeling: ☐ **Fantastic**   ☐ **Good**   ☐ **Difficult**   ☐ **Very Difficult**

Weather   Temperature: _____ ° ___   Workout Gear: _____

Notes: _____

_____

Wednesday

Date: _____   **Week 16**

Vitals: **Resting HR**: _____ bpm   **Weight**: _____ kg/lbs   Hours Slept: _____ hrs

Sport: _____   Workout: _____

Course: _____   Duration: _____   Distance: _____

Intensity: ☐ **Maximum**   ☐ **Hard**   ☐ **Medium**   ☐ **Minimum**

Average HR: _____ bpm   Target HR: _____ bpm

Feeling: ☐ **Fantastic**   ☐ **Good**   ☐ **Difficult**   ☐ **Very Difficult**

Weather   Temperature: _____ ° ___   Workout Gear: _____

Notes: _____

_____

Thursday

Date: _____   **Week 16**

Vitals: **Resting HR**: _____ bpm   **Weight**: _____ kg/lbs   Hours Slept: _____ hrs

Sport: _____   Workout: _____

Course: _____   Duration: _____   Distance: _____

Intensity: ☐ **Maximum**   ☐ **Hard**   ☐ **Medium**   ☐ **Minimum**

Average HR: _____ bpm   Target HR: _____ bpm

Feeling: ☐ **Fantastic**   ☐ **Good**   ☐ **Difficult**   ☐ **Very Difficult**

Weather   Temperature: _____ ° ___   Workout Gear: _____

Notes: _____

_____

Friday

Date: _____   **Week 16**

Vitals: **Resting HR**: _____ bpm   **Weight**: _____ kg/lbs   Hours Slept: _____ hrs

Sport: _____   Workout: _____

Course: _____   Duration: _____   Distance: _____

Intensity: ☐ **Maximum**   ☐ **Hard**   ☐ **Medium**   ☐ **Minimum**

Average HR: _____ bpm   Target HR: _____ bpm

Feeling: ☐ **Fantastic**   ☐ **Good**   ☐ **Difficult**   ☐ **Very Difficult**

Weather   Temperature: _____ ° ___   Workout Gear: _____

Notes: _____

_____

Saturday

Date: _____ **Week 16**

Vitals: **Resting HR:** _____ bpm   **Weight:** _____ kg/lbs   Hours Slept: _____ hrs

Sport: _____   Workout: _____

Course: _____   Duration: _____   Distance: _____

Intensity: ☐ **Maximum**   ☐ **Hard**   ☐ **Medium**   ☐ **Minimum**

Average HR: _____ bpm   Target HR: _____ bpm

Feeling: ☐ **Fantastic**   ☐ **Good**   ☐ **Difficult**   ☐ **Very Difficult**

Weather   Temperature: _____ ° ___   Workout Gear: _____

Notes: _____

_____

_____

Weekly Summary

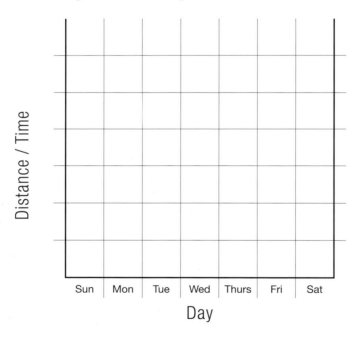

Total Time: _____   Total Distance: _____

Additional Information: _____

_____

_____

_____

_____

110

RUNNING IS **NOT** ABOUT COMPETING.
IT IS ABOUT
IMPROVING ONE'S HEALTH.
– JOHN STANTON

Sunday

Date: **Week 17**

Vitals: **Resting HR:** _____ bpm   **Weight:** _____ kg/lbs   Hours Slept: _____ hrs

Sport: _____   Workout: _____

Course: _____   Duration: _____   Distance: _____

Intensity: ☐ **Maximum**   ☐ **Hard**   ☐ **Medium**   ☐ **Minimum**

Average HR: _____ bpm   Target HR: _____ bpm

Feeling: ☐ **Fantastic**   ☐ **Good**   ☐ **Difficult**   ☐ **Very Difficult**

Weather   Temperature: _____ ° ___   Workout Gear: _____

Notes:

Monday

Date: **Week 17**

Vitals: **Resting HR:** _____ bpm   **Weight:** _____ kg/lbs   Hours Slept: _____ hrs

Sport: _____   Workout: _____

Course: _____   Duration: _____   Distance: _____

Intensity: ☐ **Maximum**   ☐ **Hard**   ☐ **Medium**   ☐ **Minimum**

Average HR: _____ bpm   Target HR: _____ bpm

Feeling: ☐ **Fantastic**   ☐ **Good**   ☐ **Difficult**   ☐ **Very Difficult**

Weather   Temperature: _____ ° ___   Workout Gear: _____

Notes:

Tuesday

Date: **Week 17**

Vitals: **Resting HR:** _____ bpm   **Weight:** _____ kg/lbs   Hours Slept: _____ hrs

Sport: _____   Workout: _____

Course: _____   Duration: _____   Distance: _____

Intensity: ☐ **Maximum**   ☐ **Hard**   ☐ **Medium**   ☐ **Minimum**

Average HR: _____ bpm   Target HR: _____ bpm

Feeling: ☐ **Fantastic**   ☐ **Good**   ☐ **Difficult**   ☐ **Very Difficult**

Weather   Temperature: _____ ° ___   Workout Gear: _____

Notes:

Wednesday

Date: _____   **Week 17**

Vitals: **Resting HR:** _____ bpm **Weight:** _____ kg/lbs Hours Slept: _____ hrs

Sport: _____   Workout: _____

Course: _____   Duration: _____   Distance: _____

Intensity: ☐ **Maximum** ☐ **Hard** ☐ **Medium** ☐ **Minimum**

Average HR: _____ bpm Target HR: _____ bpm

Feeling: ☐ **Fantastic** ☐ **Good** ☐ **Difficult** ☐ **Very Difficult**

Weather   Temperature: _____ ° ___ Workout Gear: _____

Notes: _____

_____

Thursday

Date: _____   **Week 17**

Vitals: **Resting HR:** _____ bpm **Weight:** _____ kg/lbs Hours Slept: _____ hrs

Sport: _____   Workout: _____

Course: _____   Duration: _____   Distance: _____

Intensity: ☐ **Maximum** ☐ **Hard** ☐ **Medium** ☐ **Minimum**

Average HR: _____ bpm Target HR: _____ bpm

Feeling: ☐ **Fantastic** ☐ **Good** ☐ **Difficult** ☐ **Very Difficult**

Weather   Temperature: _____ ° ___ Workout Gear: _____

Notes: _____

_____

Friday

Date: _____   **Week 17**

Vitals: **Resting HR:** _____ bpm **Weight:** _____ kg/lbs Hours Slept: _____ hrs

Sport: _____   Workout: _____

Course: _____   Duration: _____   Distance: _____

Intensity: ☐ **Maximum** ☐ **Hard** ☐ **Medium** ☐ **Minimum**

Average HR: _____ bpm Target HR: _____ bpm

Feeling: ☐ **Fantastic** ☐ **Good** ☐ **Difficult** ☐ **Very Difficult**

Weather   Temperature: _____ ° ___ Workout Gear: _____

Notes: _____

_____

Saturday

Vitals: **Resting HR**: _____ bpm   **Weight**: _____ kg/lbs   Hours Slept: _____ hrs

Sport: _____   Workout: _____

Course: _____   Duration: _____   Distance: _____

Intensity: ☐ **Maximum**   ☐ **Hard**   ☐ **Medium**   ☐ **Minimum**

Average HR: _____ bpm   Target HR: _____ bpm

Feeling: ☐ **Fantastic**   ☐ **Good**   ☐ **Difficult**   ☐ **Very Difficult**

Weather   Temperature: _____ ° ___   Workout Gear: _____

Notes:

_____

_____

Weekly Summary

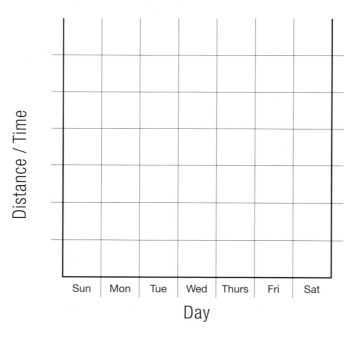

Total Time: _____   Total Distance: _____

Additional Information:

_____

_____

_____

_____

THERE'S NO SUCH THING AS
BAD WEATHER,
JUST SOFT PEOPLE.

– BILL BOWERMAN

Sunday

Date: _____   **Week 18**

Vitals: **Resting HR:** _____ bpm   **Weight:** _____ kg/lbs   Hours Slept: _____ hrs

Sport: _____   Workout: _____

Course: _____   Duration: _____   Distance: _____

Intensity: ☐ **Maximum**   ☐ **Hard**   ☐ **Medium**   ☐ **Minimum**

Average HR: _____ bpm   Target HR: _____ bpm

Feeling: ☐ **Fantastic**   ☐ **Good**   ☐ **Difficult**   ☐ **Very Difficult**

Weather   Temperature: _____ ° ___   Workout Gear: _____

Notes: _____

_____

Monday

Date: _____   **Week 18**

Vitals: **Resting HR:** _____ bpm   **Weight:** _____ kg/lbs   Hours Slept: _____ hrs

Sport: _____   Workout: _____

Course: _____   Duration: _____   Distance: _____

Intensity: ☐ **Maximum**   ☐ **Hard**   ☐ **Medium**   ☐ **Minimum**

Average HR: _____ bpm   Target HR: _____ bpm

Feeling: ☐ **Fantastic**   ☐ **Good**   ☐ **Difficult**   ☐ **Very Difficult**

Weather   Temperature: _____ ° ___   Workout Gear: _____

Notes: _____

_____

Tuesday

Date: _____   **Week 18**

Vitals: **Resting HR:** _____ bpm   **Weight:** _____ kg/lbs   Hours Slept: _____ hrs

Sport: _____   Workout: _____

Course: _____   Duration: _____   Distance: _____

Intensity: ☐ **Maximum**   ☐ **Hard**   ☐ **Medium**   ☐ **Minimum**

Average HR: _____ bpm   Target HR: _____ bpm

Feeling: ☐ **Fantastic**   ☐ **Good**   ☐ **Difficult**   ☐ **Very Difficult**

Weather   Temperature: _____ ° ___   Workout Gear: _____

Notes: _____

_____

Wednesday

Date: _____   **Week 18**

Vitals: **Resting HR**: _____ bpm   **Weight**: _____ kg/lbs   Hours Slept: _____ hrs

Sport: _____   Workout: _____

Course: _____   Duration: _____   Distance: _____

Intensity: ☐ **Maximum**   ☐ **Hard**   ☐ **Medium**   ☐ **Minimum**

Average HR: _____ bpm   Target HR: _____ bpm

Feeling: ☐ **Fantastic**   ☐ **Good**   ☐ **Difficult**   ☐ **Very Difficult**

Weather   Temperature: _____ ° ___   Workout Gear: _____

Notes: _____

_____

Thursday

Date: _____   **Week 18**

Vitals: **Resting HR**: _____ bpm   **Weight**: _____ kg/lbs   Hours Slept: _____ hrs

Sport: _____   Workout: _____

Course: _____   Duration: _____   Distance: _____

Intensity: ☐ **Maximum**   ☐ **Hard**   ☐ **Medium**   ☐ **Minimum**

Average HR: _____ bpm   Target HR: _____ bpm

Feeling: ☐ **Fantastic**   ☐ **Good**   ☐ **Difficult**   ☐ **Very Difficult**

Weather   Temperature: _____ ° ___   Workout Gear: _____

Notes: _____

_____

Friday

Date: _____   **Week 18**

Vitals: **Resting HR**: _____ bpm   **Weight**: _____ kg/lbs   Hours Slept: _____ hrs

Sport: _____   Workout: _____

Course: _____   Duration: _____   Distance: _____

Intensity: ☐ **Maximum**   ☐ **Hard**   ☐ **Medium**   ☐ **Minimum**

Average HR: _____ bpm   Target HR: _____ bpm

Feeling: ☐ **Fantastic**   ☐ **Good**   ☐ **Difficult**   ☐ **Very Difficult**

Weather   Temperature: _____ ° ___   Workout Gear: _____

Notes: _____

_____

Saturday

Vitals: **Resting HR:** _____ bpm   **Weight:** _____ kg/lbs   Hours Slept: _____ hrs

Sport: _____   Workout: _____

Course: _____   Duration: _____   Distance: _____

Intensity: ☐ **Maximum**   ☐ **Hard**   ☐ **Medium**   ☐ **Minimum**

Average HR: _____ bpm   Target HR: _____ bpm

Feeling: ☐ **Fantastic**   ☐ **Good**   ☐ **Difficult**   ☐ **Very Difficult**

Weather   Temperature: _____ ° ___   Workout Gear: _____

Notes: _____

_____

Weekly Summary

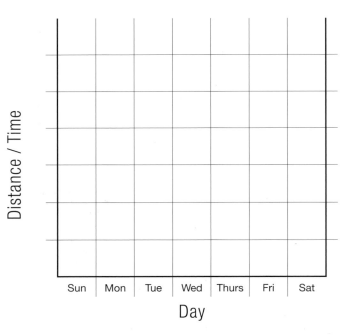

Total Time: _____   Total Distance: _____

Additional Information: _____

_____

_____

_____

RUNNING IS MY *sunshine.*

– JOAN TWINE

Sunday

Date: _____   **Week 19**

Vitals: **Resting HR:** _____ bpm   **Weight:** _____ kg/lbs   Hours Slept: _____ hrs

Sport: _____   Workout: _____

Course: _____   Duration: _____   Distance: _____

Intensity: ☐ **Maximum**   ☐ **Hard**   ☐ **Medium**   ☐ **Minimum**

Average HR: _____ bpm   Target HR: _____ bpm

Feeling: ☐ **Fantastic**   ☐ **Good**   ☐ **Difficult**   ☐ **Very Difficult**

Weather   Temperature: _____ ° ___   Workout Gear: _____

Notes: _____

_____

_____

Monday

Date: _____   **Week 19**

Vitals: **Resting HR:** _____ bpm   **Weight:** _____ kg/lbs   Hours Slept: _____ hrs

Sport: _____   Workout: _____

Course: _____   Duration: _____   Distance: _____

Intensity: ☐ **Maximum**   ☐ **Hard**   ☐ **Medium**   ☐ **Minimum**

Average HR: _____ bpm   Target HR: _____ bpm

Feeling: ☐ **Fantastic**   ☐ **Good**   ☐ **Difficult**   ☐ **Very Difficult**

Weather   Temperature: _____ ° ___   Workout Gear: _____

Notes: _____

_____

_____

Tuesday

Date: _____   **Week 19**

Vitals: **Resting HR:** _____ bpm   **Weight:** _____ kg/lbs   Hours Slept: _____ hrs

Sport: _____   Workout: _____

Course: _____   Duration: _____   Distance: _____

Intensity: ☐ **Maximum**   ☐ **Hard**   ☐ **Medium**   ☐ **Minimum**

Average HR: _____ bpm   Target HR: _____ bpm

Feeling: ☐ **Fantastic**   ☐ **Good**   ☐ **Difficult**   ☐ **Very Difficult**

Weather   Temperature: _____ ° ___   Workout Gear: _____

Notes: _____

_____

_____

Wednesday

Date: **Week 19**

Vitals: **Resting HR**: _____ bpm   **Weight**: _____ kg/lbs   Hours Slept: _____ hrs

Sport: _____   Workout: _____

Course: _____   Duration: _____   Distance: _____

Intensity: ☐ **Maximum**   ☐ **Hard**   ☐ **Medium**   ☐ **Minimum**

Average HR: _____ bpm   Target HR: _____ bpm

Feeling: ☐ **Fantastic**   ☐ **Good**   ☐ **Difficult**   ☐ **Very Difficult**

Weather   Temperature: _____ ° ___   Workout Gear: _____

Notes:

Thursday

Date: **Week 19**

Vitals: **Resting HR**: _____ bpm   **Weight**: _____ kg/lbs   Hours Slept: _____ hrs

Sport: _____   Workout: _____

Course: _____   Duration: _____   Distance: _____

Intensity: ☐ **Maximum**   ☐ **Hard**   ☐ **Medium**   ☐ **Minimum**

Average HR: _____ bpm   Target HR: _____ bpm

Feeling: ☐ **Fantastic**   ☐ **Good**   ☐ **Difficult**   ☐ **Very Difficult**

Weather   Temperature: _____ ° ___   Workout Gear: _____

Notes:

Friday

Date: **Week 19**

Vitals: **Resting HR**: _____ bpm   **Weight**: _____ kg/lbs   Hours Slept: _____ hrs

Sport: _____   Workout: _____

Course: _____   Duration: _____   Distance: _____

Intensity: ☐ **Maximum**   ☐ **Hard**   ☐ **Medium**   ☐ **Minimum**

Average HR: _____ bpm   Target HR: _____ bpm

Feeling: ☐ **Fantastic**   ☐ **Good**   ☐ **Difficult**   ☐ **Very Difficult**

Weather   Temperature: _____ ° ___   Workout Gear: _____

Notes:

Saturday

Date: _____   **Week 19**

Vitals: **Resting HR**: _____ bpm   **Weight**: _____ kg/lbs   Hours Slept: _____ hrs

Sport: _____   Workout: _____

Course: _____   Duration: _____   Distance: _____

Intensity: □ **Maximum**   □ **Hard**   □ **Medium**   □ **Minimum**

Average HR: _____ bpm   Target HR: _____ bpm

Feeling: □ **Fantastic**   □ **Good**   □ **Difficult**   □ **Very Difficult**

Weather   Temperature: _____ ° ___   Workout Gear: _____

Notes: _____

_____

_____

Weekly Summary

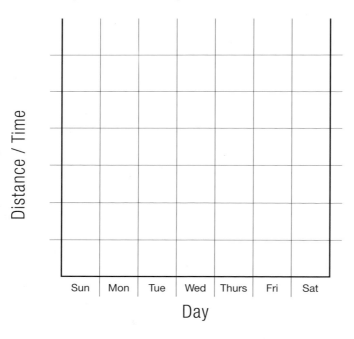

Total Time: _____   Total Distance: _____

Additional Information: _____

_____

_____

_____

_____

EVERYONE WHO HAS RUN KNOWS THAT
ITS MOST IMPORTANT VALUE IS IN
removing tension
AND ALLOWING A *release*
FROM WHATEVER CARES THE DAY MAY BRING.
- JIMMY CARTER

Sunday

Vitals: **Resting HR:** _____ bpm   **Weight:** _____ kg/lbs   Hours Slept: _____ hrs

Sport: _____   Workout: _____

Course: _____   Duration: _____   Distance: _____

Intensity: ☐ **Maximum**   ☐ **Hard**   ☐ **Medium**   ☐ **Minimum**

Average HR: _____ bpm   Target HR: _____ bpm

Feeling: ☐ **Fantastic**   ☐ **Good**   ☐ **Difficult**   ☐ **Very Difficult**

Weather   Temperature: _____ ° ___   Workout Gear: _____

Notes:

_____

_____

Monday

Vitals: **Resting HR:** _____ bpm   **Weight:** _____ kg/lbs   Hours Slept: _____ hrs

Sport: _____   Workout: _____

Course: _____   Duration: _____   Distance: _____

Intensity: ☐ **Maximum**   ☐ **Hard**   ☐ **Medium**   ☐ **Minimum**

Average HR: _____ bpm   Target HR: _____ bpm

Feeling: ☐ **Fantastic**   ☐ **Good**   ☐ **Difficult**   ☐ **Very Difficult**

Weather   Temperature: _____ ° ___   Workout Gear: _____

Notes:

_____

_____

Tuesday

Vitals: **Resting HR:** _____ bpm   **Weight:** _____ kg/lbs   Hours Slept: _____ hrs

Sport: _____   Workout: _____

Course: _____   Duration: _____   Distance: _____

Intensity: ☐ **Maximum**   ☐ **Hard**   ☐ **Medium**   ☐ **Minimum**

Average HR: _____ bpm   Target HR: _____ bpm

Feeling: ☐ **Fantastic**   ☐ **Good**   ☐ **Difficult**   ☐ **Very Difficult**

Weather   Temperature: _____ ° ___   Workout Gear: _____

Notes:

_____

_____

Wednesday

Vitals: **Resting HR:** _____ bpm   **Weight:** _____ kg/lbs   Hours Slept: _____ hrs

Sport: _____   Workout: _____

Course: _____   Duration: _____   Distance: _____

Intensity: ☐ **Maximum**   ☐ **Hard**   ☐ **Medium**   ☐ **Minimum**

Average HR: _____ bpm   Target HR: _____ bpm

Feeling: ☐ **Fantastic**   ☐ **Good**   ☐ **Difficult**   ☐ **Very Difficult**

Weather   Temperature: _____ ° __   Workout Gear: _____

Notes:

Thursday

Vitals: **Resting HR:** _____ bpm   **Weight:** _____ kg/lbs   Hours Slept: _____ hrs

Sport: _____   Workout: _____

Course: _____   Duration: _____   Distance: _____

Intensity: ☐ **Maximum**   ☐ **Hard**   ☐ **Medium**   ☐ **Minimum**

Average HR: _____ bpm   Target HR: _____ bpm

Feeling: ☐ **Fantastic**   ☐ **Good**   ☐ **Difficult**   ☐ **Very Difficult**

Weather   Temperature: _____ ° __   Workout Gear: _____

Notes:

Friday

Vitals: **Resting HR:** _____ bpm   **Weight:** _____ kg/lbs   Hours Slept: _____ hrs

Sport: _____   Workout: _____

Course: _____   Duration: _____   Distance: _____

Intensity: ☐ **Maximum**   ☐ **Hard**   ☐ **Medium**   ☐ **Minimum**

Average HR: _____ bpm   Target HR: _____ bpm

Feeling: ☐ **Fantastic**   ☐ **Good**   ☐ **Difficult**   ☐ **Very Difficult**

Weather   Temperature: _____ ° __   Workout Gear: _____

Notes:

Saturday

Date: _____   **Week 20**

Vitals: **Resting HR**: _____ bpm   **Weight**: _____ kg/lbs   Hours Slept: _____ hrs

Sport: _____   Workout: _____

Course: _____   Duration: _____   Distance: _____

Intensity: ☐ **Maximum**   ☐ **Hard**   ☐ **Medium**   ☐ **Minimum**

Average HR: _____ bpm   Target HR: _____ bpm

Feeling: ☐ **Fantastic**   ☐ **Good**   ☐ **Difficult**   ☐ **Very Difficult**

Weather   Temperature: _____ ° ___   Workout Gear: _____

Notes: _____

_____

Weekly Summary

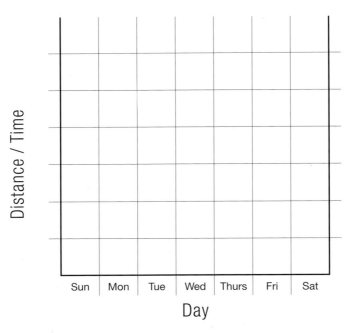

Total Time: _____   Total Distance: _____

Additional Information: _____

_____

_____

_____

YOUR ABILITY TO RUN

is a gift.

– JOHN STANTON

Sunday

Date: **Week 21**

Vitals: **Resting HR**: _____ bpm   **Weight**: _____ kg/lbs   Hours Slept: _____ hrs

Sport: _____   Workout: _____

Course: _____   Duration: _____   Distance: _____

Intensity: ☐ **Maximum**   ☐ **Hard**   ☐ **Medium**   ☐ **Minimum**

Average HR: _____ bpm   Target HR: _____ bpm

Feeling: ☐ **Fantastic**   ☐ **Good**   ☐ **Difficult**   ☐ **Very Difficult**

Weather   Temperature: _____ ° ___   Workout Gear: _____

Notes: _____

_____

Monday

Date: **Week 21**

Vitals: **Resting HR**: _____ bpm   **Weight**: _____ kg/lbs   Hours Slept: _____ hrs

Sport: _____   Workout: _____

Course: _____   Duration: _____   Distance: _____

Intensity: ☐ **Maximum**   ☐ **Hard**   ☐ **Medium**   ☐ **Minimum**

Average HR: _____ bpm   Target HR: _____ bpm

Feeling: ☐ **Fantastic**   ☐ **Good**   ☐ **Difficult**   ☐ **Very Difficult**

Weather   Temperature: _____ ° ___   Workout Gear: _____

Notes: _____

_____

Tuesday

Date: **Week 21**

Vitals: **Resting HR**: _____ bpm   **Weight**: _____ kg/lbs   Hours Slept: _____ hrs

Sport: _____   Workout: _____

Course: _____   Duration: _____   Distance: _____

Intensity: ☐ **Maximum**   ☐ **Hard**   ☐ **Medium**   ☐ **Minimum**

Average HR: _____ bpm   Target HR: _____ bpm

Feeling: ☐ **Fantastic**   ☐ **Good**   ☐ **Difficult**   ☐ **Very Difficult**

Weather   Temperature: _____ ° ___   Workout Gear: _____

Notes: _____

_____

Wednesday

Vitals: **Resting HR:** _____ bpm   **Weight:** _____ kg/lbs   Hours Slept: _____ hrs

Sport: _____   Workout: _____

Course: _____   Duration: _____   Distance: _____

Intensity: ☐ **Maximum**   ☐ **Hard**   ☐ **Medium**   ☐ **Minimum**

Average HR: _____ bpm   Target HR: _____ bpm

Feeling: ☐ **Fantastic**   ☐ **Good**   ☐ **Difficult**   ☐ **Very Difficult**

Weather   Temperature: _____ ° ___   Workout Gear: _____

Notes: _____

_____

_____

Thursday

Vitals: **Resting HR:** _____ bpm   **Weight:** _____ kg/lbs   Hours Slept: _____ hrs

Sport: _____   Workout: _____

Course: _____   Duration: _____   Distance: _____

Intensity: ☐ **Maximum**   ☐ **Hard**   ☐ **Medium**   ☐ **Minimum**

Average HR: _____ bpm   Target HR: _____ bpm

Feeling: ☐ **Fantastic**   ☐ **Good**   ☐ **Difficult**   ☐ **Very Difficult**

Weather   Temperature: _____ ° ___   Workout Gear: _____

Notes: _____

_____

_____

Friday

Vitals: **Resting HR:** _____ bpm   **Weight:** _____ kg/lbs   Hours Slept: _____ hrs

Sport: _____   Workout: _____

Course: _____   Duration: _____   Distance: _____

Intensity: ☐ **Maximum**   ☐ **Hard**   ☐ **Medium**   ☐ **Minimum**

Average HR: _____ bpm   Target HR: _____ bpm

Feeling: ☐ **Fantastic**   ☐ **Good**   ☐ **Difficult**   ☐ **Very Difficult**

Weather   Temperature: _____ ° ___   Workout Gear: _____

Notes: _____

_____

_____

Saturday

Date: _____   **Week 21**

Vitals: **Resting HR:** _____ bpm   **Weight:** _____ kg/lbs   Hours Slept: _____ hrs

Sport: _____   Workout: _____

Course: _____   Duration: _____   Distance: _____

Intensity: ☐ **Maximum**   ☐ **Hard**   ☐ **Medium**   ☐ **Minimum**

Average HR: _____ bpm   Target HR: _____ bpm

Feeling: ☐ **Fantastic**   ☐ **Good**   ☐ **Difficult**   ☐ **Very Difficult**

Weather   Temperature: _____ ° ___   Workout Gear: _____

Notes: _____

_____

_____

Weekly Summary

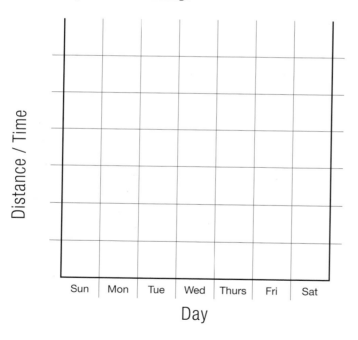

Total Time: _____   Total Distance: _____

Additional Information: _____

_____

_____

_____

_____

The race does not always go to the swift, but to the ones who keep running.

– Anonymous

Sunday

Date: _____   **Week 22**

Vitals: **Resting HR**: _____ bpm   **Weight**: _____ kg/lbs   Hours Slept: _____ hrs

Sport: _____   Workout: _____

Course: _____   Duration: _____   Distance: _____

Intensity: ☐ **Maximum**   ☐ **Hard**   ☐ **Medium**   ☐ **Minimum**

Average HR: _____ bpm   Target HR: _____ bpm

Feeling: ☐ **Fantastic**   ☐ **Good**   ☐ **Difficult**   ☐ **Very Difficult**

Weather   Temperature: _____ ° ___   Workout Gear: _____

Notes:

Monday

Date: _____   **Week 22**

Vitals: **Resting HR**: _____ bpm   **Weight**: _____ kg/lbs   Hours Slept: _____ hrs

Sport: _____   Workout: _____

Course: _____   Duration: _____   Distance: _____

Intensity: ☐ **Maximum**   ☐ **Hard**   ☐ **Medium**   ☐ **Minimum**

Average HR: _____ bpm   Target HR: _____ bpm

Feeling: ☐ **Fantastic**   ☐ **Good**   ☐ **Difficult**   ☐ **Very Difficult**

Weather   Temperature: _____ ° ___   Workout Gear: _____

Notes:

Tuesday

Date: _____   **Week 22**

Vitals: **Resting HR**: _____ bpm   **Weight**: _____ kg/lbs   Hours Slept: _____ hrs

Sport: _____   Workout: _____

Course: _____   Duration: _____   Distance: _____

Intensity: ☐ **Maximum**   ☐ **Hard**   ☐ **Medium**   ☐ **Minimum**

Average HR: _____ bpm   Target HR: _____ bpm

Feeling: ☐ **Fantastic**   ☐ **Good**   ☐ **Difficult**   ☐ **Very Difficult**

Weather   Temperature: _____ ° ___   Workout Gear: _____

Notes:

Wednesday

Date: **Week 22**

Vitals: **Resting HR:** _____ bpm   **Weight:** _____ kg/lbs   Hours Slept: _____ hrs

Sport: _____   Workout: _____

Course: _____   Duration: _____   Distance: _____

Intensity: ☐ **Maximum**   ☐ **Hard**   ☐ **Medium**   ☐ **Minimum**

Average HR: _____ bpm   Target HR: _____ bpm

Feeling: ☐ **Fantastic**   ☐ **Good**   ☐ **Difficult**   ☐ **Very Difficult**

Weather   Temperature: _____ ° ___   Workout Gear: _____

Notes:

Thursday

Date: **Week 22**

Vitals: **Resting HR:** _____ bpm   **Weight:** _____ kg/lbs   Hours Slept: _____ hrs

Sport: _____   Workout: _____

Course: _____   Duration: _____   Distance: _____

Intensity: ☐ **Maximum**   ☐ **Hard**   ☐ **Medium**   ☐ **Minimum**

Average HR: _____ bpm   Target HR: _____ bpm

Feeling: ☐ **Fantastic**   ☐ **Good**   ☐ **Difficult**   ☐ **Very Difficult**

Weather   Temperature: _____ ° ___   Workout Gear: _____

Notes:

Friday

Date: **Week 22**

Vitals: **Resting HR:** _____ bpm   **Weight:** _____ kg/lbs   Hours Slept: _____ hrs

Sport: _____   Workout: _____

Course: _____   Duration: _____   Distance: _____

Intensity: ☐ **Maximum**   ☐ **Hard**   ☐ **Medium**   ☐ **Minimum**

Average HR: _____ bpm   Target HR: _____ bpm

Feeling: ☐ **Fantastic**   ☐ **Good**   ☐ **Difficult**   ☐ **Very Difficult**

Weather   Temperature: _____ ° ___   Workout Gear: _____

Notes:

Saturday

Date: _____   **Week 22**

Vitals: **Resting HR**: _____ bpm   **Weight**: _____ kg/lbs   Hours Slept: _____ hrs

Sport: _____   Workout: _____

Course: _____   Duration: _____   Distance: _____

Intensity: ☐ **Maximum**   ☐ **Hard**   ☐ **Medium**   ☐ **Minimum**

Average HR: _____ bpm   Target HR: _____ bpm

Feeling: ☐ **Fantastic**   ☐ **Good**   ☐ **Difficult**   ☐ **Very Difficult**

Weather   Temperature: _____ ° ___   Workout Gear: _____

Notes: _____

_____

_____

Weekly Summary

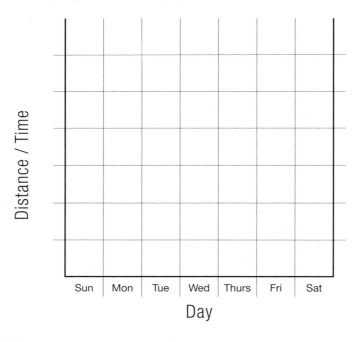

Total Time: _____   Total Distance: _____

Additional Information: _____

_____

_____

_____

_____

yourself, NOT OTHERS.

– JEFF GALLOWAY

Sunday

Date: _____   **Week 23**

Vitals: **Resting HR**: _____ bpm   **Weight**: _____ kg/lbs   Hours Slept: _____ hrs

Sport: _____   Workout: _____

Course: _____   Duration: _____   Distance: _____

Intensity: ☐ **Maximum**   ☐ **Hard**   ☐ **Medium**   ☐ **Minimum**

Average HR: _____ bpm   Target HR: _____ bpm

Feeling: ☐ **Fantastic**   ☐ **Good**   ☐ **Difficult**   ☐ **Very Difficult**

Weather   Temperature: _____ ° ___   Workout Gear: _____

Notes: _____

_____

Monday

Date: _____   **Week 23**

Vitals: **Resting HR**: _____ bpm   **Weight**: _____ kg/lbs   Hours Slept: _____ hrs

Sport: _____   Workout: _____

Course: _____   Duration: _____   Distance: _____

Intensity: ☐ **Maximum**   ☐ **Hard**   ☐ **Medium**   ☐ **Minimum**

Average HR: _____ bpm   Target HR: _____ bpm

Feeling: ☐ **Fantastic**   ☐ **Good**   ☐ **Difficult**   ☐ **Very Difficult**

Weather   Temperature: _____ ° ___   Workout Gear: _____

Notes: _____

_____

Tuesday

Date: _____   **Week 23**

Vitals: **Resting HR**: _____ bpm   **Weight**: _____ kg/lbs   Hours Slept: _____ hrs

Sport: _____   Workout: _____

Course: _____   Duration: _____   Distance: _____

Intensity: ☐ **Maximum**   ☐ **Hard**   ☐ **Medium**   ☐ **Minimum**

Average HR: _____ bpm   Target HR: _____ bpm

Feeling: ☐ **Fantastic**   ☐ **Good**   ☐ **Difficult**   ☐ **Very Difficult**

Weather   Temperature: _____ ° ___   Workout Gear: _____

Notes: _____

_____

Wednesday

Date: _____   **Week 23**

Vitals: **Resting HR:** _____ bpm **Weight:** _____ kg/lbs Hours Slept: _____ hrs

Sport: _____ Workout: _____

Course: _____ Duration: _____ Distance: _____

Intensity: ☐ **Maximum** ☐ **Hard** ☐ **Medium** ☐ **Minimum**

Average HR: _____ bpm Target HR: _____ bpm

Feeling: ☐ **Fantastic** ☐ **Good** ☐ **Difficult** ☐ **Very Difficult**

Weather   Temperature: _____ ° __ Workout Gear: _____

Notes:

Thursday

Date: _____   **Week 23**

Vitals: **Resting HR:** _____ bpm **Weight:** _____ kg/lbs Hours Slept: _____ hrs

Sport: _____ Workout: _____

Course: _____ Duration: _____ Distance: _____

Intensity: ☐ **Maximum** ☐ **Hard** ☐ **Medium** ☐ **Minimum**

Average HR: _____ bpm Target HR: _____ bpm

Feeling: ☐ **Fantastic** ☐ **Good** ☐ **Difficult** ☐ **Very Difficult**

Weather   Temperature: _____ ° __ Workout Gear: _____

Notes:

Friday

Date: _____   **Week 23**

Vitals: **Resting HR:** _____ bpm **Weight:** _____ kg/lbs Hours Slept: _____ hrs

Sport: _____ Workout: _____

Course: _____ Duration: _____ Distance: _____

Intensity: ☐ **Maximum** ☐ **Hard** ☐ **Medium** ☐ **Minimum**

Average HR: _____ bpm Target HR: _____ bpm

Feeling: ☐ **Fantastic** ☐ **Good** ☐ **Difficult** ☐ **Very Difficult**

Weather   Temperature: _____ ° __ Workout Gear: _____

Notes:

Saturday

Vitals: **Resting HR**: _____ bpm   **Weight**: _____ kg/lbs   Hours Slept: _____ hrs

Sport: _____   Workout: _____

Course: _____   Duration: _____   Distance: _____

Intensity: ☐ **Maximum**   ☐ **Hard**   ☐ **Medium**   ☐ **Minimum**

Average HR: _____ bpm   Target HR: _____ bpm

Feeling: ☐ **Fantastic**   ☐ **Good**   ☐ **Difficult**   ☐ **Very Difficult**

Weather   Temperature: _____ ° ___   Workout Gear: _____

Notes: _____

_____

Weekly Summary

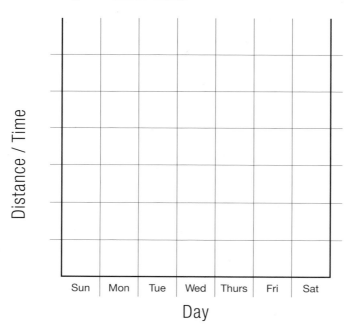

Total Time: _____   Total Distance: _____

Additional Information: _____

_____

_____

_____

All it takes is
all you got.

– Mark Davis

Sunday

Date: _____   **Week 24**

Vitals: **Resting HR**: _____ bpm   **Weight**: _____ kg/lbs   Hours Slept: _____ hrs

Sport: _____   Workout: _____

Course: _____   Duration: _____   Distance: _____

Intensity: ☐ **Maximum**   ☐ **Hard**   ☐ **Medium**   ☐ **Minimum**

Average HR: _____ bpm   Target HR: _____ bpm

Feeling: ☐ **Fantastic**   ☐ **Good**   ☐ **Difficult**   ☐ **Very Difficult**

Weather   Temperature: _____ ° ___   Workout Gear: _____

Notes:

_____

_____

Monday

Date: _____   **Week 24**

Vitals: **Resting HR**: _____ bpm   **Weight**: _____ kg/lbs   Hours Slept: _____ hrs

Sport: _____   Workout: _____

Course: _____   Duration: _____   Distance: _____

Intensity: ☐ **Maximum**   ☐ **Hard**   ☐ **Medium**   ☐ **Minimum**

Average HR: _____ bpm   Target HR: _____ bpm

Feeling: ☐ **Fantastic**   ☐ **Good**   ☐ **Difficult**   ☐ **Very Difficult**

Weather   Temperature: _____ ° ___   Workout Gear: _____

Notes:

_____

_____

Tuesday

Date: _____   **Week 24**

Vitals: **Resting HR**: _____ bpm   **Weight**: _____ kg/lbs   Hours Slept: _____ hrs

Sport: _____   Workout: _____

Course: _____   Duration: _____   Distance: _____

Intensity: ☐ **Maximum**   ☐ **Hard**   ☐ **Medium**   ☐ **Minimum**

Average HR: _____ bpm   Target HR: _____ bpm

Feeling: ☐ **Fantastic**   ☐ **Good**   ☐ **Difficult**   ☐ **Very Difficult**

Weather   Temperature: _____ ° ___   Workout Gear: _____

Notes:

_____

_____

Wednesday

Vitals: **Resting HR**: _____ bpm   **Weight**: _____ kg/lbs   Hours Slept: _____ hrs

Sport: _____   Workout: _____

Course: _____   Duration: _____   Distance: _____

Intensity: ☐ **Maximum**   ☐ **Hard**   ☐ **Medium**   ☐ **Minimum**

Average HR: _____ bpm   Target HR: _____ bpm

Feeling: ☐ **Fantastic**   ☐ **Good**   ☐ **Difficult**   ☐ **Very Difficult**

Weather   Temperature: _____ ° ___   Workout Gear: _____

Notes:

Thursday

Vitals: **Resting HR**: _____ bpm   **Weight**: _____ kg/lbs   Hours Slept: _____ hrs

Sport: _____   Workout: _____

Course: _____   Duration: _____   Distance: _____

Intensity: ☐ **Maximum**   ☐ **Hard**   ☐ **Medium**   ☐ **Minimum**

Average HR: _____ bpm   Target HR: _____ bpm

Feeling: ☐ **Fantastic**   ☐ **Good**   ☐ **Difficult**   ☐ **Very Difficult**

Weather   Temperature: _____ ° ___   Workout Gear: _____

Notes:

Friday

Vitals: **Resting HR**: _____ bpm   **Weight**: _____ kg/lbs   Hours Slept: _____ hrs

Sport: _____   Workout: _____

Course: _____   Duration: _____   Distance: _____

Intensity: ☐ **Maximum**   ☐ **Hard**   ☐ **Medium**   ☐ **Minimum**

Average HR: _____ bpm   Target HR: _____ bpm

Feeling: ☐ **Fantastic**   ☐ **Good**   ☐ **Difficult**   ☐ **Very Difficult**

Weather   Temperature: _____ ° ___   Workout Gear: _____

Notes:

Saturday

Date: _____   **Week 24**

Vitals: **Resting HR**: _____ bpm   **Weight**: _____ kg/lbs   Hours Slept: _____ hrs

Sport: _____   Workout: _____

Course: _____   Duration: _____   Distance: _____

Intensity: ☐ **Maximum**   ☐ **Hard**   ☐ **Medium**   ☐ **Minimum**

Average HR: _____ bpm   Target HR: _____ bpm

Feeling: ☐ **Fantastic**   ☐ **Good**   ☐ **Difficult**   ☐ **Very Difficult**

Weather   Temperature: _____ ° ___   Workout Gear: _____

Notes:
_____
_____

Weekly Summary

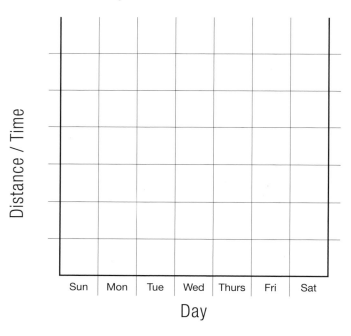

Total Time: _____   Total Distance: _____

Additional Information:
_____
_____
_____
_____

Do it and it becomes a *passion.*

- John Stanton

Sunday

Vitals: **Resting HR**: _____ bpm   **Weight**: _____ kg/lbs   Hours Slept: _____ hrs

Sport: _____   Workout: _____

Course: _____   Duration: _____   Distance: _____

Intensity: ☐ **Maximum**   ☐ **Hard**   ☐ **Medium**   ☐ **Minimum**

Average HR: _____ bpm   Target HR: _____ bpm

Feeling: ☐ **Fantastic**   ☐ **Good**   ☐ **Difficult**   ☐ **Very Difficult**

Weather   Temperature: _____ ° ___   Workout Gear: _____

Notes: _____

_____

Monday

Vitals: **Resting HR**: _____ bpm   **Weight**: _____ kg/lbs   Hours Slept: _____ hrs

Sport: _____   Workout: _____

Course: _____   Duration: _____   Distance: _____

Intensity: ☐ **Maximum**   ☐ **Hard**   ☐ **Medium**   ☐ **Minimum**

Average HR: _____ bpm   Target HR: _____ bpm

Feeling: ☐ **Fantastic**   ☐ **Good**   ☐ **Difficult**   ☐ **Very Difficult**

Weather   Temperature: _____ ° ___   Workout Gear: _____

Notes: _____

_____

Tuesday

Vitals: **Resting HR**: _____ bpm   **Weight**: _____ kg/lbs   Hours Slept: _____ hrs

Sport: _____   Workout: _____

Course: _____   Duration: _____   Distance: _____

Intensity: ☐ **Maximum**   ☐ **Hard**   ☐ **Medium**   ☐ **Minimum**

Average HR: _____ bpm   Target HR: _____ bpm

Feeling: ☐ **Fantastic**   ☐ **Good**   ☐ **Difficult**   ☐ **Very Difficult**

Weather   Temperature: _____ ° ___   Workout Gear: _____

Notes: _____

_____

Wednesday

Date: _____   **Week 25**

Vitals: **Resting HR:** _____ bpm   **Weight:** _____ kg/lbs   Hours Slept: _____ hrs

Sport: _____   Workout: _____

Course: _____   Duration: _____   Distance: _____

Intensity: ☐ **Maximum**   ☐ **Hard**   ☐ **Medium**   ☐ **Minimum**

Average HR: _____ bpm   Target HR: _____ bpm

Feeling: ☐ **Fantastic**   ☐ **Good**   ☐ **Difficult**   ☐ **Very Difficult**

Weather   Temperature: _____ ° ___   Workout Gear: _____

Notes:

Thursday

Date: _____   **Week 25**

Vitals: **Resting HR:** _____ bpm   **Weight:** _____ kg/lbs   Hours Slept: _____ hrs

Sport: _____   Workout: _____

Course: _____   Duration: _____   Distance: _____

Intensity: ☐ **Maximum**   ☐ **Hard**   ☐ **Medium**   ☐ **Minimum**

Average HR: _____ bpm   Target HR: _____ bpm

Feeling: ☐ **Fantastic**   ☐ **Good**   ☐ **Difficult**   ☐ **Very Difficult**

Weather   Temperature: _____ ° ___   Workout Gear: _____

Notes:

Friday

Date: _____   **Week 25**

Vitals: **Resting HR:** _____ bpm   **Weight:** _____ kg/lbs   Hours Slept: _____ hrs

Sport: _____   Workout: _____

Course: _____   Duration: _____   Distance: _____

Intensity: ☐ **Maximum**   ☐ **Hard**   ☐ **Medium**   ☐ **Minimum**

Average HR: _____ bpm   Target HR: _____ bpm

Feeling: ☐ **Fantastic**   ☐ **Good**   ☐ **Difficult**   ☐ **Very Difficult**

Weather   Temperature: _____ ° ___   Workout Gear: _____

Notes:

Saturday

Date: _____   **Week 25**

Vitals: **Resting HR:** _____ bpm   **Weight:** _____ kg/lbs   Hours Slept: _____ hrs

Sport: _____   Workout: _____

Course: _____   Duration: _____   Distance: _____

Intensity: ☐ **Maximum**   ☐ **Hard**   ☐ **Medium**   ☐ **Minimum**

Average HR: _____ bpm   Target HR: _____ bpm

Feeling: ☐ **Fantastic**   ☐ **Good**   ☐ **Difficult**   ☐ **Very Difficult**

Weather   Temperature: _____ ° ___   Workout Gear: _____

Notes: _____

_____

Weekly Summary

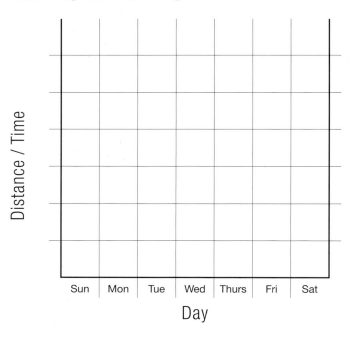

Total Time: _____   Total Distance: _____

Additional Information: _____

_____

_____

_____

ONE OF THE BEST THINGS ABOUT
RUNNING IS ALL THE FRIENDS
you meet along the way.

– JOHN STANTON

Sunday

Date: _____   **Week 26**

Vitals: **Resting HR**: _____ bpm   **Weight**: _____ kg/lbs   Hours Slept: _____ hrs

Sport: _____   Workout: _____

Course: _____   Duration: _____   Distance: _____

Intensity: ☐ **Maximum**   ☐ **Hard**   ☐ **Medium**   ☐ **Minimum**

Average HR: _____ bpm   Target HR: _____ bpm

Feeling: ☐ **Fantastic**   ☐ **Good**   ☐ **Difficult**   ☐ **Very Difficult**

Weather   Temperature: _____ ° ___   Workout Gear: _____

Notes:

_____

_____

Monday

Date: _____   **Week 26**

Vitals: **Resting HR**: _____ bpm   **Weight**: _____ kg/lbs   Hours Slept: _____ hrs

Sport: _____   Workout: _____

Course: _____   Duration: _____   Distance: _____

Intensity: ☐ **Maximum**   ☐ **Hard**   ☐ **Medium**   ☐ **Minimum**

Average HR: _____ bpm   Target HR: _____ bpm

Feeling: ☐ **Fantastic**   ☐ **Good**   ☐ **Difficult**   ☐ **Very Difficult**

Weather   Temperature: _____ ° ___   Workout Gear: _____

Notes:

_____

_____

Tuesday

Date: _____   **Week 26**

Vitals: **Resting HR**: _____ bpm   **Weight**: _____ kg/lbs   Hours Slept: _____ hrs

Sport: _____   Workout: _____

Course: _____   Duration: _____   Distance: _____

Intensity: ☐ **Maximum**   ☐ **Hard**   ☐ **Medium**   ☐ **Minimum**

Average HR: _____ bpm   Target HR: _____ bpm

Feeling: ☐ **Fantastic**   ☐ **Good**   ☐ **Difficult**   ☐ **Very Difficult**

Weather   Temperature: _____ ° ___   Workout Gear: _____

Notes:

_____

_____

Wednesday

Date: _____   **Week 26**

Vitals: **Resting HR:** _____ bpm   **Weight:** _____ kg/lbs   Hours Slept: _____ hrs

Sport: _____   Workout: _____

Course: _____   Duration: _____   Distance: _____

Intensity: ☐ **Maximum**   ☐ **Hard**   ☐ **Medium**   ☐ **Minimum**

Average HR: _____ bpm   Target HR: _____ bpm

Feeling: ☐ **Fantastic**   ☐ **Good**   ☐ **Difficult**   ☐ **Very Difficult**

Weather   Temperature: _____ ° ___   Workout Gear: _____

Notes: _____

_____

_____

Thursday

Date: _____   **Week 26**

Vitals: **Resting HR:** _____ bpm   **Weight:** _____ kg/lbs   Hours Slept: _____ hrs

Sport: _____   Workout: _____

Course: _____   Duration: _____   Distance: _____

Intensity: ☐ **Maximum**   ☐ **Hard**   ☐ **Medium**   ☐ **Minimum**

Average HR: _____ bpm   Target HR: _____ bpm

Feeling: ☐ **Fantastic**   ☐ **Good**   ☐ **Difficult**   ☐ **Very Difficult**

Weather   Temperature: _____ ° ___   Workout Gear: _____

Notes: _____

_____

_____

Friday

Date: _____   **Week 26**

Vitals: **Resting HR:** _____ bpm   **Weight:** _____ kg/lbs   Hours Slept: _____ hrs

Sport: _____   Workout: _____

Course: _____   Duration: _____   Distance: _____

Intensity: ☐ **Maximum**   ☐ **Hard**   ☐ **Medium**   ☐ **Minimum**

Average HR: _____ bpm   Target HR: _____ bpm

Feeling: ☐ **Fantastic**   ☐ **Good**   ☐ **Difficult**   ☐ **Very Difficult**

Weather   Temperature: _____ ° ___   Workout Gear: _____

Notes: _____

_____

_____

Saturday

Date: _____   **Week 26**

Vitals: **Resting HR**: _____ bpm   **Weight**: _____ kg/lbs   Hours Slept: _____ hrs

Sport: _____   Workout: _____

Course: _____   Duration: _____   Distance: _____

Intensity: ☐ **Maximum**   ☐ **Hard**   ☐ **Medium**   ☐ **Minimum**

Average HR: _____ bpm   Target HR: _____ bpm

Feeling: ☐ **Fantastic**   ☐ **Good**   ☐ **Difficult**   ☐ **Very Difficult**

Weather   Temperature: _____ ° ___   Workout Gear: _____

Notes: _____
_____
_____

Weekly Summary

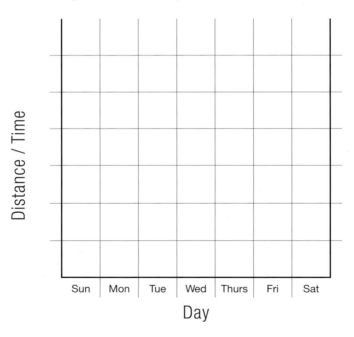

Total Time: _____   Total Distance: _____

Additional Information: _____
_____
_____
_____
_____

We should not let our fears
hold us back from **pursuing**
our hopes.

– John F. Kennedy

Sunday

Vitals: **Resting HR:** _____ bpm   **Weight:** _____ kg/lbs   Hours Slept: _____ hrs

Sport: _____   Workout: _____

Course: _____   Duration: _____   Distance: _____

Intensity: ☐ **Maximum**   ☐ **Hard**   ☐ **Medium**   ☐ **Minimum**

Average HR: _____ bpm   Target HR: _____ bpm

Feeling: ☐ **Fantastic**   ☐ **Good**   ☐ **Difficult**   ☐ **Very Difficult**

Weather   Temperature: _____ ° ___   Workout Gear: _____

Notes:

Monday

Vitals: **Resting HR:** _____ bpm   **Weight:** _____ kg/lbs   Hours Slept: _____ hrs

Sport: _____   Workout: _____

Course: _____   Duration: _____   Distance: _____

Intensity: ☐ **Maximum**   ☐ **Hard**   ☐ **Medium**   ☐ **Minimum**

Average HR: _____ bpm   Target HR: _____ bpm

Feeling: ☐ **Fantastic**   ☐ **Good**   ☐ **Difficult**   ☐ **Very Difficult**

Weather   Temperature: _____ ° ___   Workout Gear: _____

Notes:

Tuesday

Vitals: **Resting HR:** _____ bpm   **Weight:** _____ kg/lbs   Hours Slept: _____ hrs

Sport: _____   Workout: _____

Course: _____   Duration: _____   Distance: _____

Intensity: ☐ **Maximum**   ☐ **Hard**   ☐ **Medium**   ☐ **Minimum**

Average HR: _____ bpm   Target HR: _____ bpm

Feeling: ☐ **Fantastic**   ☐ **Good**   ☐ **Difficult**   ☐ **Very Difficult**

Weather   Temperature: _____ ° ___   Workout Gear: _____

Notes:

Wednesday

Date: Week 27

Vitals: **Resting HR**: _____ bpm   **Weight**: _____ kg/lbs   Hours Slept: _____ hrs

Sport: _____   Workout: _____

Course: _____   Duration: _____   Distance: _____

Intensity: ☐ **Maximum**   ☐ **Hard**   ☐ **Medium**   ☐ **Minimum**

Average HR: _____ bpm   Target HR: _____ bpm

Feeling: ☐ **Fantastic**   ☐ **Good**   ☐ **Difficult**   ☐ **Very Difficult**

Weather   Temperature: _____ ° ___   Workout Gear: _____

Notes:

Thursday

Date: Week 27

Vitals: **Resting HR**: _____ bpm   **Weight**: _____ kg/lbs   Hours Slept: _____ hrs

Sport: _____   Workout: _____

Course: _____   Duration: _____   Distance: _____

Intensity: ☐ **Maximum**   ☐ **Hard**   ☐ **Medium**   ☐ **Minimum**

Average HR: _____ bpm   Target HR: _____ bpm

Feeling: ☐ **Fantastic**   ☐ **Good**   ☐ **Difficult**   ☐ **Very Difficult**

Weather   Temperature: _____ ° ___   Workout Gear: _____

Notes:

Friday

Date: Week 27

Vitals: **Resting HR**: _____ bpm   **Weight**: _____ kg/lbs   Hours Slept: _____ hrs

Sport: _____   Workout: _____

Course: _____   Duration: _____   Distance: _____

Intensity: ☐ **Maximum**   ☐ **Hard**   ☐ **Medium**   ☐ **Minimum**

Average HR: _____ bpm   Target HR: _____ bpm

Feeling: ☐ **Fantastic**   ☐ **Good**   ☐ **Difficult**   ☐ **Very Difficult**

Weather   Temperature: _____ ° ___   Workout Gear: _____

Notes:

Saturday

Date: _____ **Week 27**

Vitals: **Resting HR:** _____ bpm   **Weight:** _____ kg/lbs   Hours Slept: _____ hrs

Sport: _____   Workout: _____

Course: _____   Duration: _____   Distance: _____

Intensity: ☐ **Maximum**   ☐ **Hard**   ☐ **Medium**   ☐ **Minimum**

Average HR: _____ bpm   Target HR: _____ bpm

Feeling: ☐ **Fantastic**   ☐ **Good**   ☐ **Difficult**   ☐ **Very Difficult**

Weather   Temperature: _____ ° ___   Workout Gear: _____

Notes: _____

_____

Weekly Summary

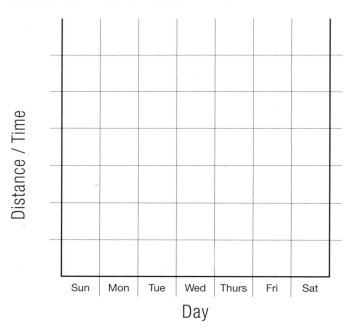

Total Time: _____   Total Distance: _____

Additional Information: _____

_____

_____

_____

154

EVERY DAY IS A GOOD DAY
when you run.

– KEVIN NELSON

Sunday

Date: _____   **Week 28**

Vitals: **Resting HR**: _____ bpm   **Weight**: _____ kg/lbs   Hours Slept: _____ hrs

Sport: _____   Workout: _____

Course: _____   Duration: _____   Distance: _____

Intensity: ☐ **Maximum**   ☐ **Hard**   ☐ **Medium**   ☐ **Minimum**

Average HR: _____ bpm   Target HR: _____ bpm

Feeling: ☐ **Fantastic**   ☐ **Good**   ☐ **Difficult**   ☐ **Very Difficult**

Weather   Temperature: _____ ° ___   Workout Gear: _____

Notes: _____

_____

Monday

Date: _____   **Week 28**

Vitals: **Resting HR**: _____ bpm   **Weight**: _____ kg/lbs   Hours Slept: _____ hrs

Sport: _____   Workout: _____

Course: _____   Duration: _____   Distance: _____

Intensity: ☐ **Maximum**   ☐ **Hard**   ☐ **Medium**   ☐ **Minimum**

Average HR: _____ bpm   Target HR: _____ bpm

Feeling: ☐ **Fantastic**   ☐ **Good**   ☐ **Difficult**   ☐ **Very Difficult**

Weather   Temperature: _____ ° ___   Workout Gear: _____

Notes: _____

_____

Tuesday

Date: _____   **Week 28**

Vitals: **Resting HR**: _____ bpm   **Weight**: _____ kg/lbs   Hours Slept: _____ hrs

Sport: _____   Workout: _____

Course: _____   Duration: _____   Distance: _____

Intensity: ☐ **Maximum**   ☐ **Hard**   ☐ **Medium**   ☐ **Minimum**

Average HR: _____ bpm   Target HR: _____ bpm

Feeling: ☐ **Fantastic**   ☐ **Good**   ☐ **Difficult**   ☐ **Very Difficult**

Weather   Temperature: _____ ° ___   Workout Gear: _____

Notes: _____

_____

Wednesday

Date: _____   **Week 28**

Vitals: **Resting HR:** _____ bpm   **Weight:** _____ kg/lbs   Hours Slept: _____ hrs

Sport: _____   Workout: _____

Course: _____   Duration: _____   Distance: _____

Intensity: ☐ **Maximum**   ☐ **Hard**   ☐ **Medium**   ☐ **Minimum**

Average HR: _____ bpm   Target HR: _____ bpm

Feeling: ☐ **Fantastic**   ☐ **Good**   ☐ **Difficult**   ☐ **Very Difficult**

Weather   Temperature: _____ ° ___   Workout Gear: _____

Notes: _____

_____

Thursday

Date: _____   **Week 28**

Vitals: **Resting HR:** _____ bpm   **Weight:** _____ kg/lbs   Hours Slept: _____ hrs

Sport: _____   Workout: _____

Course: _____   Duration: _____   Distance: _____

Intensity: ☐ **Maximum**   ☐ **Hard**   ☐ **Medium**   ☐ **Minimum**

Average HR: _____ bpm   Target HR: _____ bpm

Feeling: ☐ **Fantastic**   ☐ **Good**   ☐ **Difficult**   ☐ **Very Difficult**

Weather   Temperature: _____ ° ___   Workout Gear: _____

Notes: _____

_____

Friday

Date: _____   **Week 28**

Vitals: **Resting HR:** _____ bpm   **Weight:** _____ kg/lbs   Hours Slept: _____ hrs

Sport: _____   Workout: _____

Course: _____   Duration: _____   Distance: _____

Intensity: ☐ **Maximum**   ☐ **Hard**   ☐ **Medium**   ☐ **Minimum**

Average HR: _____ bpm   Target HR: _____ bpm

Feeling: ☐ **Fantastic**   ☐ **Good**   ☐ **Difficult**   ☐ **Very Difficult**

Weather   Temperature: _____ ° ___   Workout Gear: _____

Notes: _____

_____

Saturday

Vitals: **Resting HR**: _____ bpm   **Weight**: _____ kg/lbs   Hours Slept: _____ hrs

Sport: _____   Workout: _____

Course: _____   Duration: _____   Distance: _____

Intensity: ☐ **Maximum**   ☐ **Hard**   ☐ **Medium**   ☐ **Minimum**

Average HR: _____ bpm   Target HR: _____ bpm

Feeling: ☐ **Fantastic**   ☐ **Good**   ☐ **Difficult**   ☐ **Very Difficult**

Weather   Temperature: _____ ° ___   Workout Gear: _____

Notes: _____

_____

_____

Weekly Summary

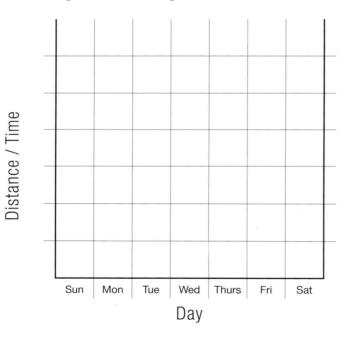

Total Time: _____   Total Distance: _____

Additional Information: _____

_____

_____

_____

Desire
IS THE MOST IMPORTANT FACTOR IN THE SUCCESS OF ANY ATHLETE.

- WILLIE SHOEMAKER

Sunday

Date: _____   **Week 29**

Vitals: **Resting HR**: _____ bpm   **Weight**: _____ kg/lbs   Hours Slept: _____ hrs

Sport: _____   Workout: _____

Course: _____   Duration: _____   Distance: _____

Intensity: ☐ **Maximum**   ☐ **Hard**   ☐ **Medium**   ☐ **Minimum**

Average HR: _____ bpm   Target HR: _____ bpm

Feeling: ☐ **Fantastic**   ☐ **Good**   ☐ **Difficult**   ☐ **Very Difficult**

Weather   Temperature: _____ ° ___   Workout Gear: _____

Notes: _____

_____

_____

Monday

Date: _____   **Week 29**

Vitals: **Resting HR**: _____ bpm   **Weight**: _____ kg/lbs   Hours Slept: _____ hrs

Sport: _____   Workout: _____

Course: _____   Duration: _____   Distance: _____

Intensity: ☐ **Maximum**   ☐ **Hard**   ☐ **Medium**   ☐ **Minimum**

Average HR: _____ bpm   Target HR: _____ bpm

Feeling: ☐ **Fantastic**   ☐ **Good**   ☐ **Difficult**   ☐ **Very Difficult**

Weather   Temperature: _____ ° ___   Workout Gear: _____

Notes: _____

_____

_____

Tuesday

Date: _____   **Week 29**

Vitals: **Resting HR**: _____ bpm   **Weight**: _____ kg/lbs   Hours Slept: _____ hrs

Sport: _____   Workout: _____

Course: _____   Duration: _____   Distance: _____

Intensity: ☐ **Maximum**   ☐ **Hard**   ☐ **Medium**   ☐ **Minimum**

Average HR: _____ bpm   Target HR: _____ bpm

Feeling: ☐ **Fantastic**   ☐ **Good**   ☐ **Difficult**   ☐ **Very Difficult**

Weather   Temperature: _____ ° ___   Workout Gear: _____

Notes: _____

_____

_____

Wednesday

Date: _____ **Week 29**

Vitals: **Resting HR:** _____ bpm **Weight:** _____ kg/lbs Hours Slept: _____ hrs

Sport: _____ Workout: _____

Course: _____ Duration: _____ Distance: _____

Intensity: ☐ **Maximum** ☐ **Hard** ☐ **Medium** ☐ **Minimum**

Average HR: _____ bpm Target HR: _____ bpm

Feeling: ☐ **Fantastic** ☐ **Good** ☐ **Difficult** ☐ **Very Difficult**

Weather Temperature: _____ ° ___ Workout Gear: _____

Notes:

Thursday

Date: _____ **Week 29**

Vitals: **Resting HR:** _____ bpm **Weight:** _____ kg/lbs Hours Slept: _____ hrs

Sport: _____ Workout: _____

Course: _____ Duration: _____ Distance: _____

Intensity: ☐ **Maximum** ☐ **Hard** ☐ **Medium** ☐ **Minimum**

Average HR: _____ bpm Target HR: _____ bpm

Feeling: ☐ **Fantastic** ☐ **Good** ☐ **Difficult** ☐ **Very Difficult**

Weather Temperature: _____ ° ___ Workout Gear: _____

Notes:

Friday

Date: _____ **Week 29**

Vitals: **Resting HR:** _____ bpm **Weight:** _____ kg/lbs Hours Slept: _____ hrs

Sport: _____ Workout: _____

Course: _____ Duration: _____ Distance: _____

Intensity: ☐ **Maximum** ☐ **Hard** ☐ **Medium** ☐ **Minimum**

Average HR: _____ bpm Target HR: _____ bpm

Feeling: ☐ **Fantastic** ☐ **Good** ☐ **Difficult** ☐ **Very Difficult**

Weather Temperature: _____ ° ___ Workout Gear: _____

Notes:

Saturday

Date: _____   **Week 29**

Vitals: **Resting HR:** _____ bpm   **Weight:** _____ kg/lbs   Hours Slept: _____ hrs

Sport: _____   Workout: _____

Course: _____   Duration: _____   Distance: _____

Intensity: ☐ **Maximum**   ☐ **Hard**   ☐ **Medium**   ☐ **Minimum**

Average HR: _____ bpm   Target HR: _____ bpm

Feeling: ☐ **Fantastic**   ☐ **Good**   ☐ **Difficult**   ☐ **Very Difficult**

Weather   Temperature: _____ ° ___   Workout Gear: _____

Notes:

_____

_____

Weekly Summary

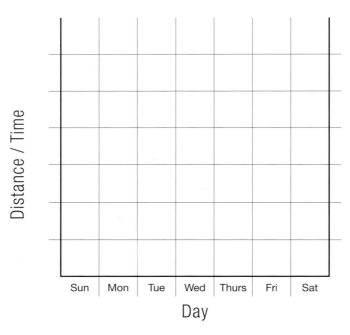

Total Time: _____   Total Distance: _____

Additional Information:

_____

_____

_____

_____

RUNNING IS THE
GREATEST METAPHOR FOR LIFE,
BECAUSE YOU GET OUT OF IT
WHAT YOU PUT INTO IT.
– OPRAH WINFREY

Sunday

Vitals: **Resting HR**: _____ bpm   **Weight**: _____ kg/lbs   Hours Slept: _____ hrs

Sport: _____   Workout: _____

Course: _____   Duration: _____   Distance: _____

Intensity: ☐ **Maximum**   ☐ **Hard**   ☐ **Medium**   ☐ **Minimum**

Average HR: _____ bpm   Target HR: _____ bpm

Feeling: ☐ **Fantastic**   ☐ **Good**   ☐ **Difficult**   ☐ **Very Difficult**

Weather   Temperature: _____ ° ___   Workout Gear: _____

Notes:

_____

_____

Monday

Vitals: **Resting HR**: _____ bpm   **Weight**: _____ kg/lbs   Hours Slept: _____ hrs

Sport: _____   Workout: _____

Course: _____   Duration: _____   Distance: _____

Intensity: ☐ **Maximum**   ☐ **Hard**   ☐ **Medium**   ☐ **Minimum**

Average HR: _____ bpm   Target HR: _____ bpm

Feeling: ☐ **Fantastic**   ☐ **Good**   ☐ **Difficult**   ☐ **Very Difficult**

Weather   Temperature: _____ ° ___   Workout Gear: _____

Notes:

_____

_____

Tuesday

Vitals: **Resting HR**: _____ bpm   **Weight**: _____ kg/lbs   Hours Slept: _____ hrs

Sport: _____   Workout: _____

Course: _____   Duration: _____   Distance: _____

Intensity: ☐ **Maximum**   ☐ **Hard**   ☐ **Medium**   ☐ **Minimum**

Average HR: _____ bpm   Target HR: _____ bpm

Feeling: ☐ **Fantastic**   ☐ **Good**   ☐ **Difficult**   ☐ **Very Difficult**

Weather   Temperature: _____ ° ___   Workout Gear: _____

Notes:

_____

_____

Wednesday

Vitals: **Resting HR**: _____ bpm   **Weight**: _____ kg/lbs   Hours Slept: _____ hrs

Sport: _____   Workout: _____

Course: _____   Duration: _____   Distance: _____

Intensity: ☐ **Maximum**   ☐ **Hard**   ☐ **Medium**   ☐ **Minimum**

Average HR: _____ bpm   Target HR: _____ bpm

Feeling: ☐ **Fantastic**   ☐ **Good**   ☐ **Difficult**   ☐ **Very Difficult**

Weather   Temperature: _____ ° ___   Workout Gear: _____

Notes:

Thursday

Vitals: **Resting HR**: _____ bpm   **Weight**: _____ kg/lbs   Hours Slept: _____ hrs

Sport: _____   Workout: _____

Course: _____   Duration: _____   Distance: _____

Intensity: ☐ **Maximum**   ☐ **Hard**   ☐ **Medium**   ☐ **Minimum**

Average HR: _____ bpm   Target HR: _____ bpm

Feeling: ☐ **Fantastic**   ☐ **Good**   ☐ **Difficult**   ☐ **Very Difficult**

Weather   Temperature: _____ ° ___   Workout Gear: _____

Notes:

Friday

Vitals: **Resting HR**: _____ bpm   **Weight**: _____ kg/lbs   Hours Slept: _____ hrs

Sport: _____   Workout: _____

Course: _____   Duration: _____   Distance: _____

Intensity: ☐ **Maximum**   ☐ **Hard**   ☐ **Medium**   ☐ **Minimum**

Average HR: _____ bpm   Target HR: _____ bpm

Feeling: ☐ **Fantastic**   ☐ **Good**   ☐ **Difficult**   ☐ **Very Difficult**

Weather   Temperature: _____ ° ___   Workout Gear: _____

Notes:

Saturday

Date: _____   **Week 30**

Vitals: **Resting HR**: _____ bpm   **Weight**: _____ kg/lbs   Hours Slept: _____ hrs

Sport: _____   Workout: _____

Course: _____   Duration: _____   Distance: _____

Intensity: ☐ **Maximum**   ☐ **Hard**   ☐ **Medium**   ☐ **Minimum**

Average HR: _____ bpm   Target HR: _____ bpm

Feeling: ☐ **Fantastic**   ☐ **Good**   ☐ **Difficult**   ☐ **Very Difficult**

Weather   Temperature: _____ ° ___   Workout Gear: _____

Notes: _____

_____

_____

Weekly Summary

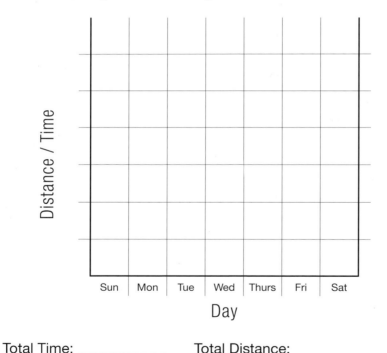

Total Time: _____   Total Distance: _____

Additional Information: _____

_____

_____

_____

_____

DON'T BE AFRAID TO TAKE A
BIG STEP IF ONE IS INDICATED.
YOU CAN'T CROSS A CHASM IN TWO SMALL JUMPS.

— DAVID LLOYD GEORGE

Sunday

Date: _____   **Week 31**

Vitals: **Resting HR**: _____ bpm   **Weight**: _____ kg/lbs   Hours Slept: _____ hrs

Sport: _____   Workout: _____

Course: _____   Duration: _____   Distance: _____

Intensity: ☐ **Maximum**   ☐ **Hard**   ☐ **Medium**   ☐ **Minimum**

Average HR: _____ bpm   Target HR: _____ bpm

Feeling: ☐ **Fantastic**   ☐ **Good**   ☐ **Difficult**   ☐ **Very Difficult**

Weather   Temperature: _____ ° ___   Workout Gear: _____

Notes: _____

_____

_____

Monday

Date: _____   **Week 31**

Vitals: **Resting HR**: _____ bpm   **Weight**: _____ kg/lbs   Hours Slept: _____ hrs

Sport: _____   Workout: _____

Course: _____   Duration: _____   Distance: _____

Intensity: ☐ **Maximum**   ☐ **Hard**   ☐ **Medium**   ☐ **Minimum**

Average HR: _____ bpm   Target HR: _____ bpm

Feeling: ☐ **Fantastic**   ☐ **Good**   ☐ **Difficult**   ☐ **Very Difficult**

Weather   Temperature: _____ ° ___   Workout Gear: _____

Notes: _____

_____

_____

Tuesday

Date: _____   **Week 31**

Vitals: **Resting HR**: _____ bpm   **Weight**: _____ kg/lbs   Hours Slept: _____ hrs

Sport: _____   Workout: _____

Course: _____   Duration: _____   Distance: _____

Intensity: ☐ **Maximum**   ☐ **Hard**   ☐ **Medium**   ☐ **Minimum**

Average HR: _____ bpm   Target HR: _____ bpm

Feeling: ☐ **Fantastic**   ☐ **Good**   ☐ **Difficult**   ☐ **Very Difficult**

Weather   Temperature: _____ ° ___   Workout Gear: _____

Notes: _____

_____

_____

Wednesday

Date: _____   **Week 31**

Vitals: **Resting HR**: _____ bpm   **Weight**: _____ kg/lbs   Hours Slept: _____ hrs

Sport: _____   Workout: _____

Course: _____   Duration: _____   Distance: _____

Intensity: ☐ **Maximum**   ☐ **Hard**   ☐ **Medium**   ☐ **Minimum**

Average HR: _____ bpm   Target HR: _____ bpm

Feeling: ☐ **Fantastic**   ☐ **Good**   ☐ **Difficult**   ☐ **Very Difficult**

Weather   Temperature: _____ ° ___   Workout Gear: _____

Notes: _____

_____

_____

Thursday

Date: _____   **Week 31**

Vitals: **Resting HR**: _____ bpm   **Weight**: _____ kg/lbs   Hours Slept: _____ hrs

Sport: _____   Workout: _____

Course: _____   Duration: _____   Distance: _____

Intensity: ☐ **Maximum**   ☐ **Hard**   ☐ **Medium**   ☐ **Minimum**

Average HR: _____ bpm   Target HR: _____ bpm

Feeling: ☐ **Fantastic**   ☐ **Good**   ☐ **Difficult**   ☐ **Very Difficult**

Weather   Temperature: _____ ° ___   Workout Gear: _____

Notes: _____

_____

_____

Friday

Date: _____   **Week 31**

Vitals: **Resting HR**: _____ bpm   **Weight**: _____ kg/lbs   Hours Slept: _____ hrs

Sport: _____   Workout: _____

Course: _____   Duration: _____   Distance: _____

Intensity: ☐ **Maximum**   ☐ **Hard**   ☐ **Medium**   ☐ **Minimum**

Average HR: _____ bpm   Target HR: _____ bpm

Feeling: ☐ **Fantastic**   ☐ **Good**   ☐ **Difficult**   ☐ **Very Difficult**

Weather   Temperature: _____ ° ___   Workout Gear: _____

Notes: _____

_____

_____

Saturday

Date: _____   **Week 31**

Vitals: **Resting HR:** _____ bpm   **Weight:** _____ kg/lbs   Hours Slept: _____ hrs

Sport: _____   Workout: _____

Course: _____   Duration: _____   Distance: _____

Intensity: ☐ **Maximum**   ☐ **Hard**   ☐ **Medium**   ☐ **Minimum**

Average HR: _____ bpm   Target HR: _____ bpm

Feeling: ☐ **Fantastic**   ☐ **Good**   ☐ **Difficult**   ☐ **Very Difficult**

Weather   Temperature: _____ ° ___   Workout Gear: _____

Notes: _____

_____

Weekly Summary

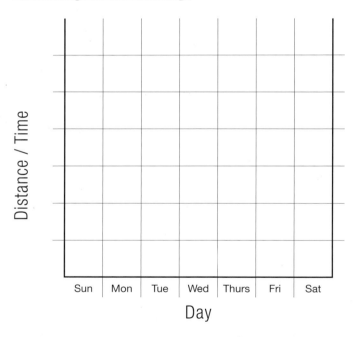

Total Time: _____   Total Distance: _____

Additional Information: _____

_____

_____

_____

MY FEELING IS THAT ANY DAY I AM
TOO BUSY TO RUN IS A DAY THAT
I AM TOO BUSY.

- JOHN BRYANT

Sunday

Vitals: **Resting HR**: _____ bpm   **Weight**: _____ kg/lbs   Hours Slept: _____ hrs

Sport: _____   Workout: _____

Course: _____   Duration: _____   Distance: _____

Intensity: ☐ **Maximum**   ☐ **Hard**   ☐ **Medium**   ☐ **Minimum**

Average HR: _____ bpm   Target HR: _____ bpm

Feeling: ☐ **Fantastic**   ☐ **Good**   ☐ **Difficult**   ☐ **Very Difficult**

Weather   Temperature: _____ ° ___   Workout Gear: _____

Notes: _____

_____

_____

Monday

Vitals: **Resting HR**: _____ bpm   **Weight**: _____ kg/lbs   Hours Slept: _____ hrs

Sport: _____   Workout: _____

Course: _____   Duration: _____   Distance: _____

Intensity: ☐ **Maximum**   ☐ **Hard**   ☐ **Medium**   ☐ **Minimum**

Average HR: _____ bpm   Target HR: _____ bpm

Feeling: ☐ **Fantastic**   ☐ **Good**   ☐ **Difficult**   ☐ **Very Difficult**

Weather   Temperature: _____ ° ___   Workout Gear: _____

Notes: _____

_____

_____

Tuesday

Vitals: **Resting HR**: _____ bpm   **Weight**: _____ kg/lbs   Hours Slept: _____ hrs

Sport: _____   Workout: _____

Course: _____   Duration: _____   Distance: _____

Intensity: ☐ **Maximum**   ☐ **Hard**   ☐ **Medium**   ☐ **Minimum**

Average HR: _____ bpm   Target HR: _____ bpm

Feeling: ☐ **Fantastic**   ☐ **Good**   ☐ **Difficult**   ☐ **Very Difficult**

Weather   Temperature: _____ ° ___   Workout Gear: _____

Notes: _____

_____

_____

Wednesday

Date: _____   **Week 32**

Vitals: **Resting HR**: _____ bpm   **Weight**: _____ kg/lbs   Hours Slept: _____ hrs

Sport: _____   Workout: _____

Course: _____   Duration: _____   Distance: _____

Intensity: ☐ **Maximum**   ☐ **Hard**   ☐ **Medium**   ☐ **Minimum**

Average HR: _____ bpm   Target HR: _____ bpm

Feeling: ☐ **Fantastic**   ☐ **Good**   ☐ **Difficult**   ☐ **Very Difficult**

Weather   Temperature: _____ ° ___   Workout Gear: _____

Notes: _____

_____

Thursday

Date: _____   **Week 32**

Vitals: **Resting HR**: _____ bpm   **Weight**: _____ kg/lbs   Hours Slept: _____ hrs

Sport: _____   Workout: _____

Course: _____   Duration: _____   Distance: _____

Intensity: ☐ **Maximum**   ☐ **Hard**   ☐ **Medium**   ☐ **Minimum**

Average HR: _____ bpm   Target HR: _____ bpm

Feeling: ☐ **Fantastic**   ☐ **Good**   ☐ **Difficult**   ☐ **Very Difficult**

Weather   Temperature: _____ ° ___   Workout Gear: _____

Notes: _____

_____

Friday

Date: _____   **Week 32**

Vitals: **Resting HR**: _____ bpm   **Weight**: _____ kg/lbs   Hours Slept: _____ hrs

Sport: _____   Workout: _____

Course: _____   Duration: _____   Distance: _____

Intensity: ☐ **Maximum**   ☐ **Hard**   ☐ **Medium**   ☐ **Minimum**

Average HR: _____ bpm   Target HR: _____ bpm

Feeling: ☐ **Fantastic**   ☐ **Good**   ☐ **Difficult**   ☐ **Very Difficult**

Weather   Temperature: _____ ° ___   Workout Gear: _____

Notes: _____

_____

Saturday

Date: _____ **Week 32**

Vitals: **Resting HR**: _____ bpm **Weight**: _____ kg/lbs Hours Slept: _____ hrs

Sport: _____ Workout: _____

Course: _____ Duration: _____ Distance: _____

Intensity: ☐ **Maximum** ☐ **Hard** ☐ **Medium** ☐ **Minimum**

Average HR: _____ bpm Target HR: _____ bpm

Feeling: ☐ **Fantastic** ☐ **Good** ☐ **Difficult** ☐ **Very Difficult**

Weather Temperature: _____ ° __ Workout Gear: _____

Notes: _____
_____
_____

Weekly Summary

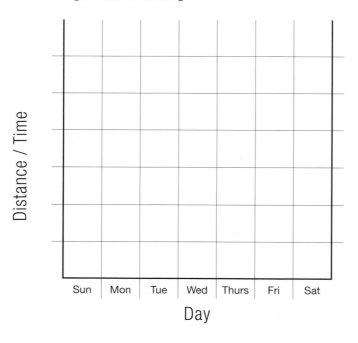

Total Time: _____ Total Distance: _____

Additional Information: _____
_____
_____
_____
_____

EVERYTHING I KNOW ABOUT LIFE,
LEARNED IT FROM *running.*

– RUBEN TOLEDO ROSADO

Sunday

Vitals: **Resting HR**: _____ bpm   **Weight**: _____ kg/lbs   Hours Slept: _____ hrs

Sport: _____   Workout: _____

Course: _____   Duration: _____   Distance: _____

Intensity: ☐ **Maximum**   ☐ **Hard**   ☐ **Medium**   ☐ **Minimum**

Average HR: _____ bpm   Target HR: _____ bpm

Feeling: ☐ **Fantastic**   ☐ **Good**   ☐ **Difficult**   ☐ **Very Difficult**

Weather   Temperature: _____ ° ___   Workout Gear: _____

Notes:

_____

_____

Monday

Vitals: **Resting HR**: _____ bpm   **Weight**: _____ kg/lbs   Hours Slept: _____ hrs

Sport: _____   Workout: _____

Course: _____   Duration: _____   Distance: _____

Intensity: ☐ **Maximum**   ☐ **Hard**   ☐ **Medium**   ☐ **Minimum**

Average HR: _____ bpm   Target HR: _____ bpm

Feeling: ☐ **Fantastic**   ☐ **Good**   ☐ **Difficult**   ☐ **Very Difficult**

Weather   Temperature: _____ ° ___   Workout Gear: _____

Notes:

_____

_____

Tuesday

Vitals: **Resting HR**: _____ bpm   **Weight**: _____ kg/lbs   Hours Slept: _____ hrs

Sport: _____   Workout: _____

Course: _____   Duration: _____   Distance: _____

Intensity: ☐ **Maximum**   ☐ **Hard**   ☐ **Medium**   ☐ **Minimum**

Average HR: _____ bpm   Target HR: _____ bpm

Feeling: ☐ **Fantastic**   ☐ **Good**   ☐ **Difficult**   ☐ **Very Difficult**

Weather   Temperature: _____ °   Workout Gear: _____

Notes:

_____

_____

Wednesday

Date: _____ **Week 33**

Vitals: **Resting HR:** _____ bpm **Weight:** _____ kg/lbs Hours Slept: _____ hrs

Sport: _____ Workout: _____

Course: _____ Duration: _____ Distance: _____

Intensity: ☐ **Maximum** ☐ **Hard** ☐ **Medium** ☐ **Minimum**

Average HR: _____ bpm Target HR: _____ bpm

Feeling: ☐ **Fantastic** ☐ **Good** ☐ **Difficult** ☐ **Very Difficult**

Weather Temperature: _____ ° ___ Workout Gear: _____

Notes:

Thursday

Date: _____ **Week 33**

Vitals: **Resting HR:** _____ bpm **Weight:** _____ kg/lbs Hours Slept: _____ hrs

Sport: _____ Workout: _____

Course: _____ Duration: _____ Distance: _____

Intensity: ☐ **Maximum** ☐ **Hard** ☐ **Medium** ☐ **Minimum**

Average HR: _____ bpm Target HR: _____ bpm

Feeling: ☐ **Fantastic** ☐ **Good** ☐ **Difficult** ☐ **Very Difficult**

Weather Temperature: _____ ° ___ Workout Gear: _____

Notes:

Friday

Date: _____ **Week 33**

Vitals: **Resting HR:** _____ bpm **Weight:** _____ kg/lbs Hours Slept: _____ hrs

Sport: _____ Workout: _____

Course: _____ Duration: _____ Distance: _____

Intensity: ☐ **Maximum** ☐ **Hard** ☐ **Medium** ☐ **Minimum**

Average HR: _____ bpm Target HR: _____ bpm

Feeling: ☐ **Fantastic** ☐ **Good** ☐ **Difficult** ☐ **Very Difficult**

Weather Temperature: _____ ° ___ Workout Gear: _____

Notes:

Saturday

Date: **Week 33**

Vitals: **Resting HR:** _____ bpm   **Weight:** _____ kg/lbs   Hours Slept: _____ hrs

Sport: _____   Workout: _____

Course: _____   Duration: _____   Distance: _____

Intensity: ☐ **Maximum**   ☐ **Hard**   ☐ **Medium**   ☐ **Minimum**

Average HR: _____ bpm   Target HR: _____ bpm

Feeling: ☐ **Fantastic**   ☐ **Good**   ☐ **Difficult**   ☐ **Very Difficult**

Weather   Temperature: _____ ° ___   Workout Gear: _____

Notes: _____

_____

Weekly Summary

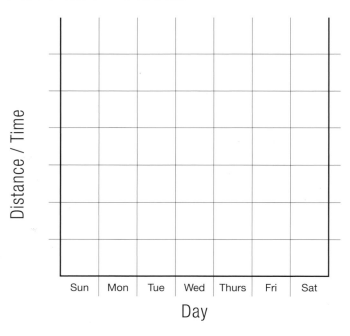

Total Time: _____   Total Distance: _____

Additional Information: _____

_____

_____

_____

Success COMES BEFORE *work* ONLY IN THE DICTIONARY.

– ANONYMOUS

Photo: Scott Soulis

Saturday

Date: _____   **Week 34**

Vitals: **Resting HR**: _____ bpm   **Weight**: _____ kg/lbs   Hours Slept: _____ hrs

Sport: _____   Workout: _____

Course: _____   Duration: _____   Distance: _____

Intensity: ☐ **Maximum**   ☐ **Hard**   ☐ **Medium**   ☐ **Minimum**

Average HR: _____ bpm   Target HR: _____ bpm

Feeling: ☐ **Fantastic**   ☐ **Good**   ☐ **Difficult**   ☐ **Very Difficult**

Weather   Temperature: _____ ° ___   Workout Gear: _____

Notes: _____

_____

Weekly Summary

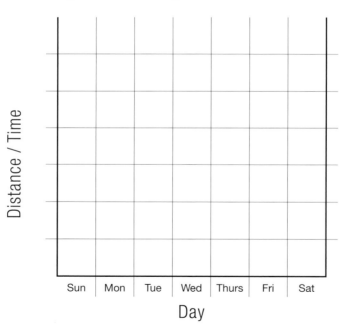

Total Time: _____   Total Distance: _____

Additional Information: _____

_____

_____

_____

_____

THE *BEST WAY OUT* IS *ALWAYS*
THROUGH.

—ROBERT FROST

Sunday

Vitals: **Resting HR:** _____ bpm   **Weight:** _____ kg/lbs   Hours Slept: _____ hrs

Sport: _____   Workout: _____

Course: _____   Duration: _____   Distance: _____

Intensity: ☐ **Maximum**   ☐ **Hard**   ☐ **Medium**   ☐ **Minimum**

Average HR: _____ bpm   Target HR: _____ bpm

Feeling: ☐ **Fantastic**   ☐ **Good**   ☐ **Difficult**   ☐ **Very Difficult**

Weather   Temperature: _____ ° __   Workout Gear: _____

Notes:

Monday

Vitals: **Resting HR:** _____ bpm   **Weight:** _____ kg/lbs   Hours Slept: _____ hrs

Sport: _____   Workout: _____

Course: _____   Duration: _____   Distance: _____

Intensity: ☐ **Maximum**   ☐ **Hard**   ☐ **Medium**   ☐ **Minimum**

Average HR: _____ bpm   Target HR: _____ bpm

Feeling: ☐ **Fantastic**   ☐ **Good**   ☐ **Difficult**   ☐ **Very Difficult**

Weather   Temperature: _____ ° __   Workout Gear: _____

Notes:

Tuesday

Vitals: **Resting HR:** _____ bpm   **Weight:** _____ kg/lbs   Hours Slept: _____ hrs

Sport: _____   Workout: _____

Course: _____   Duration: _____   Distance: _____

Intensity: ☐ **Maximum**   ☐ **Hard**   ☐ **Medium**   ☐ **Minimum**

Average HR: _____ bpm   Target HR: _____ bpm

Feeling: ☐ **Fantastic**   ☐ **Good**   ☐ **Difficult**   ☐ **Very Difficult**

Weather   Temperature: _____ ° __   Workout Gear: _____

Notes:

Wednesday

Vitals: **Resting HR**: _____ bpm   **Weight**: _____ kg/lbs   Hours Slept: _____ hrs

Sport: _____   Workout: _____

Course: _____   Duration: _____   Distance: _____

Intensity: ☐ **Maximum**   ☐ **Hard**   ☐ **Medium**   ☐ **Minimum**

Average HR: _____ bpm   Target HR: _____ bpm

Feeling: ☐ **Fantastic**   ☐ **Good**   ☐ **Difficult**   ☐ **Very Difficult**

Weather   Temperature: _____ ° ___   Workout Gear: _____

Notes:

Thursday

Vitals: **Resting HR**: _____ bpm   **Weight**: _____ kg/lbs   Hours Slept: _____ hrs

Sport: _____   Workout: _____

Course: _____   Duration: _____   Distance: _____

Intensity: ☐ **Maximum**   ☐ **Hard**   ☐ **Medium**   ☐ **Minimum**

Average HR: _____ bpm   Target HR: _____ bpm

Feeling: ☐ **Fantastic**   ☐ **Good**   ☐ **Difficult**   ☐ **Very Difficult**

Weather   Temperature: _____ ° ___   Workout Gear: _____

Notes:

Friday

Vitals: **Resting HR**: _____ bpm   **Weight**: _____ kg/lbs   Hours Slept: _____ hrs

Sport: _____   Workout: _____

Course: _____   Duration: _____   Distance: _____

Intensity: ☐ **Maximum**   ☐ **Hard**   ☐ **Medium**   ☐ **Minimum**

Average HR: _____ bpm   Target HR: _____ bpm

Feeling: ☐ **Fantastic**   ☐ **Good**   ☐ **Difficult**   ☐ **Very Difficult**

Weather   Temperature: _____ ° ___   Workout Gear: _____

Notes:

Saturday

Date: _____   **Week 35**

Vitals: **Resting HR**: _____ bpm   **Weight**: _____ kg/lbs   Hours Slept: _____ hrs

Sport: _____   Workout: _____

Course: _____   Duration: _____   Distance: _____

Intensity: ☐ **Maximum**   ☐ **Hard**   ☐ **Medium**   ☐ **Minimum**

Average HR: _____ bpm   Target HR: _____ bpm

Feeling: ☐ **Fantastic**   ☐ **Good**   ☐ **Difficult**   ☐ **Very Difficult**

Weather   Temperature: _____ ° ___   Workout Gear: _____

Notes: _____

_____

_____

Weekly Summary

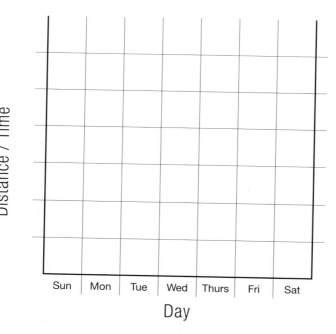

Total Time: _____   Total Distance: _____

Additional Information: _____

_____

_____

_____

_____

Nothing's better than
the wind to your back,
the sun in front of you
and your friends beside you.

– Aaron Douglas Trimble

Sunday

Vitals: **Resting HR**: _____ bpm   **Weight**: _____ kg/lbs   Hours Slept: _____ hrs

Sport: _____   Workout: _____

Course: _____   Duration: _____   Distance: _____

Intensity: ☐ **Maximum**   ☐ **Hard**   ☐ **Medium**   ☐ **Minimum**

Average HR: _____ bpm   Target HR: _____ bpm

Feeling: ☐ **Fantastic**   ☐ **Good**   ☐ **Difficult**   ☐ **Very Difficult**

Weather   Temperature: _____ ° ___   Workout Gear: _____

Notes:

Monday

Vitals: **Resting HR**: _____ bpm   **Weight**: _____ kg/lbs   Hours Slept: _____ hrs

Sport: _____   Workout: _____

Course: _____   Duration: _____   Distance: _____

Intensity: ☐ **Maximum**   ☐ **Hard**   ☐ **Medium**   ☐ **Minimum**

Average HR: _____ bpm   Target HR: _____ bpm

Feeling: ☐ **Fantastic**   ☐ **Good**   ☐ **Difficult**   ☐ **Very Difficult**

Weather   Temperature: _____ ° ___   Workout Gear: _____

Notes:

Tuesday

Vitals: **Resting HR**: _____ bpm   **Weight**: _____ kg/lbs   Hours Slept: _____ hrs

Sport: _____   Workout: _____

Course: _____   Duration: _____   Distance: _____

Intensity: ☐ **Maximum**   ☐ **Hard**   ☐ **Medium**   ☐ **Minimum**

Average HR: _____ bpm   Target HR: _____ bpm

Feeling: ☐ **Fantastic**   ☐ **Good**   ☐ **Difficult**   ☐ **Very Difficult**

Weather   Temperature: _____ ° ___   Workout Gear: _____

Notes:

Wednesday

Vitals: **Resting HR:** _____ bpm   **Weight:** _____ kg/lbs   Hours Slept: _____ hrs

Sport: _____   Workout: _____

Course: _____   Duration: _____   Distance: _____

Intensity: ☐ **Maximum**   ☐ **Hard**   ☐ **Medium**   ☐ **Minimum**

Average HR: _____ bpm   Target HR: _____ bpm

Feeling: ☐ **Fantastic**   ☐ **Good**   ☐ **Difficult**   ☐ **Very Difficult**

Weather   Temperature: _____ ° ___   Workout Gear: _____

Notes:

Thursday

Vitals: **Resting HR:** _____ bpm   **Weight:** _____ kg/lbs   Hours Slept: _____ hrs

Sport: _____   Workout: _____

Course: _____   Duration: _____   Distance: _____

Intensity: ☐ **Maximum**   ☐ **Hard**   ☐ **Medium**   ☐ **Minimum**

Average HR: _____ bpm   Target HR: _____ bpm

Feeling: ☐ **Fantastic**   ☐ **Good**   ☐ **Difficult**   ☐ **Very Difficult**

Weather   Temperature: _____ ° ___   Workout Gear: _____

Notes:

Friday

Vitals: **Resting HR:** _____ bpm   **Weight:** _____ kg/lbs   Hours Slept: _____ hrs

Sport: _____   Workout: _____

Course: _____   Duration: _____   Distance: _____

Intensity: ☐ **Maximum**   ☐ **Hard**   ☐ **Medium**   ☐ **Minimum**

Average HR: _____ bpm   Target HR: _____ bpm

Feeling: ☐ **Fantastic**   ☐ **Good**   ☐ **Difficult**   ☐ **Very Difficult**

Weather   Temperature: _____ ° ___   Workout Gear: _____

Notes:

Saturday

Date: _____ **Week 36**

Vitals: **Resting HR**: _____ bpm **Weight**: _____ kg/lbs Hours Slept: _____ hrs

Sport: _____ Workout: _____

Course: _____ Duration: _____ Distance: _____

Intensity: ☐ **Maximum** ☐ **Hard** ☐ **Medium** ☐ **Minimum**

Average HR: _____ bpm Target HR: _____ bpm

Feeling: ☐ **Fantastic** ☐ **Good** ☐ **Difficult** ☐ **Very Difficult**

Weather Temperature: _____ ° ___ Workout Gear: _____

Notes: _____

_____

Weekly Summary

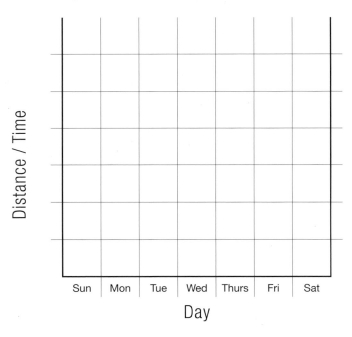

Total Time: _____ Total Distance: _____

Additional Information: _____

_____

_____

_____

Do not let what you
cannot do interfere with
what you *can* do.

- *John Wooden*

Sunday

Date: _____   **Week 37**

Vitals: **Resting HR:** _____ bpm   **Weight:** _____ kg/lbs   Hours Slept: _____ hrs

Sport: _____   Workout: _____

Course: _____   Duration: _____   Distance: _____

Intensity: ☐ **Maximum**   ☐ **Hard**   ☐ **Medium**   ☐ **Minimum**

Average HR: _____ bpm   Target HR: _____ bpm

Feeling: ☐ **Fantastic**   ☐ **Good**   ☐ **Difficult**   ☐ **Very Difficult**

Weather   Temperature: _____ ° ___   Workout Gear: _____

Notes: _____

_____

Monday

Date: _____   **Week 37**

Vitals: **Resting HR:** _____ bpm   **Weight:** _____ kg/lbs   Hours Slept: _____ hrs

Sport: _____   Workout: _____

Course: _____   Duration: _____   Distance: _____

Intensity: ☐ **Maximum**   ☐ **Hard**   ☐ **Medium**   ☐ **Minimum**

Average HR: _____ bpm   Target HR: _____ bpm

Feeling: ☐ **Fantastic**   ☐ **Good**   ☐ **Difficult**   ☐ **Very Difficult**

Weather   Temperature: _____ ° ___   Workout Gear: _____

Notes: _____

_____

Tuesday

Date: _____   **Week 37**

Vitals: **Resting HR:** _____ bpm   **Weight:** _____ kg/lbs   Hours Slept: _____ hrs

Sport: _____   Workout: _____

Course: _____   Duration: _____   Distance: _____

Intensity: ☐ **Maximum**   ☐ **Hard**   ☐ **Medium**   ☐ **Minimum**

Average HR: _____ bpm   Target HR: _____ bpm

Feeling: ☐ **Fantastic**   ☐ **Good**   ☐ **Difficult**   ☐ **Very Difficult**

Weather   Temperature: _____ ° ___   Workout Gear: _____

Notes: _____

_____

Wednesday

Date: _____   **Week 37**

Vitals: **Resting HR:** _____ bpm   **Weight:** _____ kg/lbs   Hours Slept: _____ hrs

Sport: _____   Workout: _____

Course: _____   Duration: _____   Distance: _____

Intensity: ☐ **Maximum**   ☐ **Hard**   ☐ **Medium**   ☐ **Minimum**

Average HR: _____ bpm   Target HR: _____ bpm

Feeling: ☐ **Fantastic**   ☐ **Good**   ☐ **Difficult**   ☐ **Very Difficult**

Weather   Temperature: _____ ° ___   Workout Gear: _____

Notes:

Thursday

Date: _____   **Week 37**

Vitals: **Resting HR:** _____ bpm   **Weight:** _____ kg/lbs   Hours Slept: _____ hrs

Sport: _____   Workout: _____

Course: _____   Duration: _____   Distance: _____

Intensity: ☐ **Maximum**   ☐ **Hard**   ☐ **Medium**   ☐ **Minimum**

Average HR: _____ bpm   Target HR: _____ bpm

Feeling: ☐ **Fantastic**   ☐ **Good**   ☐ **Difficult**   ☐ **Very Difficult**

Weather   Temperature: _____ ° ___   Workout Gear: _____

Notes:

Friday

Date: _____   **Week 37**

Vitals: **Resting HR:** _____ bpm   **Weight:** _____ kg/lbs   Hours Slept: _____ hrs

Sport: _____   Workout: _____

Course: _____   Duration: _____   Distance: _____

Intensity: ☐ **Maximum**   ☐ **Hard**   ☐ **Medium**   ☐ **Minimum**

Average HR: _____ bpm   Target HR: _____ bpm

Feeling: ☐ **Fantastic**   ☐ **Good**   ☐ **Difficult**   ☐ **Very Difficult**

Weather   Temperature: _____ ° ___   Workout Gear: _____

Notes:

Saturday

Date: _____   **Week 37**

Vitals: **Resting HR**: _____ bpm   **Weight**: _____ kg/lbs   Hours Slept: _____ hrs

Sport: _____   Workout: _____

Course: _____   Duration: _____   Distance: _____

Intensity: ☐ **Maximum**   ☐ **Hard**   ☐ **Medium**   ☐ **Minimum**

Average HR: _____ bpm   Target HR: _____ bpm

Feeling: ☐ **Fantastic**   ☐ **Good**   ☐ **Difficult**   ☐ **Very Difficult**

Weather   Temperature: _____ ° ___   Workout Gear: _____

Notes: _____

_____

Weekly Summary

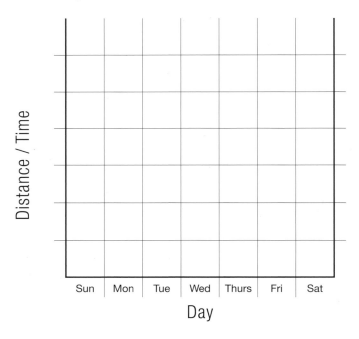

Total Time: _____   Total Distance: _____

Additional Information: _____

_____

_____

_____

194

Big **results** require big **ambitions.**

- James Champy

Sunday

Vitals: **Resting HR**: _____ bpm   **Weight**: _____ kg/lbs   Hours Slept: _____ hrs

Sport: _____   Workout: _____

Course: _____   Duration: _____   Distance: _____

Intensity: ☐ **Maximum**   ☐ **Hard**   ☐ **Medium**   ☐ **Minimum**

Average HR: _____ bpm   Target HR: _____ bpm

Feeling: ☐ **Fantastic**   ☐ **Good**   ☐ **Difficult**   ☐ **Very Difficult**

Weather   Temperature: _____ ° ___   Workout Gear: _____

Notes: _____

_____

Monday

Vitals: **Resting HR**: _____ bpm   **Weight**: _____ kg/lbs   Hours Slept: _____ hrs

Sport: _____   Workout: _____

Course: _____   Duration: _____   Distance: _____

Intensity: ☐ **Maximum**   ☐ **Hard**   ☐ **Medium**   ☐ **Minimum**

Average HR: _____ bpm   Target HR: _____ bpm

Feeling: ☐ **Fantastic**   ☐ **Good**   ☐ **Difficult**   ☐ **Very Difficult**

Weather   Temperature: _____ ° ___   Workout Gear: _____

Notes: _____

_____

Tuesday

Vitals: **Resting HR**: _____ bpm   **Weight**: _____ kg/lbs   Hours Slept: _____ hrs

Sport: _____   Workout: _____

Course: _____   Duration: _____   Distance: _____

Intensity: ☐ **Maximum**   ☐ **Hard**   ☐ **Medium**   ☐ **Minimum**

Average HR: _____ bpm   Target HR: _____ bpm

Feeling: ☐ **Fantastic**   ☐ **Good**   ☐ **Difficult**   ☐ **Very Difficult**

Weather   Temperature: _____ ° ___   Workout Gear: _____

Notes: _____

_____

Wednesday

Date: **Week 38**

Vitals: **Resting HR**: _____ bpm   **Weight**: _____ kg/lbs   Hours Slept: _____ hrs

Sport: _____   Workout: _____

Course: _____   Duration: _____   Distance: _____

Intensity: ☐ **Maximum**   ☐ **Hard**   ☐ **Medium**   ☐ **Minimum**

Average HR: _____ bpm   Target HR: _____ bpm

Feeling: ☐ **Fantastic**   ☐ **Good**   ☐ **Difficult**   ☐ **Very Difficult**

Weather   Temperature: _____ ° ___   Workout Gear: _____

Notes:

Thursday

Date: **Week 38**

Vitals: **Resting HR**: _____ bpm   **Weight**: _____ kg/lbs   Hours Slept: _____ hrs

Sport: _____   Workout: _____

Course: _____   Duration: _____   Distance: _____

Intensity: ☐ **Maximum**   ☐ **Hard**   ☐ **Medium**   ☐ **Minimum**

Average HR: _____ bpm   Target HR: _____ bpm

Feeling: ☐ **Fantastic**   ☐ **Good**   ☐ **Difficult**   ☐ **Very Difficult**

Weather   Temperature: _____ ° ___   Workout Gear: _____

Notes:

Friday

Date: **Week 38**

Vitals: **Resting HR**: _____ bpm   **Weight**: _____ kg/lbs   Hours Slept: _____ hrs

Sport: _____   Workout: _____

Course: _____   Duration: _____   Distance: _____

Intensity: ☐ **Maximum**   ☐ **Hard**   ☐ **Medium**   ☐ **Minimum**

Average HR: _____ bpm   Target HR: _____ bpm

Feeling: ☐ **Fantastic**   ☐ **Good**   ☐ **Difficult**   ☐ **Very Difficult**

Weather   Temperature: _____ ° ___   Workout Gear: _____

Notes:

Saturday

Vitals: **Resting HR**: _____ bpm   **Weight**: _____ kg/lbs   Hours Slept: _____ hrs

Sport: _____   Workout: _____

Course: _____   Duration: _____   Distance: _____

Intensity: □ **Maximum**   □ **Hard**   □ **Medium**   □ **Minimum**

Average HR: _____ bpm   Target HR: _____ bpm

Feeling: □ **Fantastic**   □ **Good**   □ **Difficult**   □ **Very Difficult**

Weather   Temperature: _____ ° ___   Workout Gear: _____

Notes: _____

_____

Weekly Summary

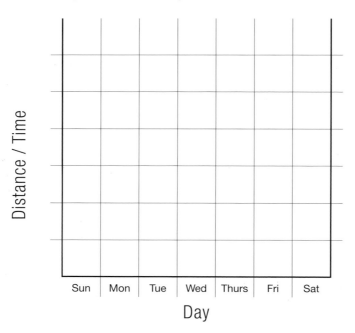

Total Time: _____   Total Distance: _____

Additional Information:

_____

_____

_____

_____

We all have dreams.
BUT IN ORDER TO MAKE DREAMS COME
INTO REALITY, IT TAKES AN AWFUL LOT OF
determination, dedication,
self-discipline & effort.
-JESSE OWENS

Sunday
Date: _____   **Week 39**

Vitals: **Resting HR:** _____ bpm   **Weight:** _____ kg/lbs   Hours Slept: _____ hrs

Sport: _____   Workout: _____

Course: _____   Duration: _____   Distance: _____

Intensity: ☐ **Maximum**   ☐ **Hard**   ☐ **Medium**   ☐ **Minimum**

Average HR: _____ bpm   Target HR: _____ bpm

Feeling: ☐ **Fantastic**   ☐ **Good**   ☐ **Difficult**   ☐ **Very Difficult**

Weather   Temperature: _____ ° ___   Workout Gear: _____

Notes: _____

_____

Monday
Date: _____   **Week 39**

Vitals: **Resting HR:** _____ bpm   **Weight:** _____ kg/lbs   Hours Slept: _____ hrs

Sport: _____   Workout: _____

Course: _____   Duration: _____   Distance: _____

Intensity: ☐ **Maximum**   ☐ **Hard**   ☐ **Medium**   ☐ **Minimum**

Average HR: _____ bpm   Target HR: _____ bpm

Feeling: ☐ **Fantastic**   ☐ **Good**   ☐ **Difficult**   ☐ **Very Difficult**

Weather   Temperature: _____ ° ___   Workout Gear: _____

Notes: _____

_____

Tuesday
Date: _____   **Week 39**

Vitals: **Resting HR:** _____ bpm   **Weight:** _____ kg/lbs   Hours Slept: _____ hrs

Sport: _____   Workout: _____

Course: _____   Duration: _____   Distance: _____

Intensity: ☐ **Maximum**   ☐ **Hard**   ☐ **Medium**   ☐ **Minimum**

Average HR: _____ bpm   Target HR: _____ bpm

Feeling: ☐ **Fantastic**   ☐ **Good**   ☐ **Difficult**   ☐ **Very Difficult**

Weather   Temperature: _____ ° ___   Workout Gear: _____

Notes: _____

_____

Wednesday

Vitals: **Resting HR**: _____ bpm   **Weight**: _____ kg/lbs   Hours Slept: _____ hrs

Sport: _____   Workout: _____

Course: _____   Duration: _____   Distance: _____

Intensity: ☐ **Maximum**   ☐ **Hard**   ☐ **Medium**   ☐ **Minimum**

Average HR: _____ bpm   Target HR: _____ bpm

Feeling: ☐ **Fantastic**   ☐ **Good**   ☐ **Difficult**   ☐ **Very Difficult**

Weather   Temperature: _____ ° ___   Workout Gear: _____

Notes: _____

_____

Thursday

Vitals: **Resting HR**: _____ bpm   **Weight**: _____ kg/lbs   Hours Slept: _____ hrs

Sport: _____   Workout: _____

Course: _____   Duration: _____   Distance: _____

Intensity: ☐ **Maximum**   ☐ **Hard**   ☐ **Medium**   ☐ **Minimum**

Average HR: _____ bpm   Target HR: _____ bpm

Feeling: ☐ **Fantastic**   ☐ **Good**   ☐ **Difficult**   ☐ **Very Difficult**

Weather   Temperature: _____ ° ___   Workout Gear: _____

Notes: _____

_____

Friday

Vitals: **Resting HR**: _____ bpm   **Weight**: _____ kg/lbs   Hours Slept: _____ hrs

Sport: _____   Workout: _____

Course: _____   Duration: _____   Distance: _____

Intensity: ☐ **Maximum**   ☐ **Hard**   ☐ **Medium**   ☐ **Minimum**

Average HR: _____ bpm   Target HR: _____ bpm

Feeling: ☐ **Fantastic**   ☐ **Good**   ☐ **Difficult**   ☐ **Very Difficult**

Weather   Temperature: _____ ° ___   Workout Gear: _____

Notes: _____

_____

Saturday

Date: _____   **Week 39**

Vitals: **Resting HR**: _____ bpm   **Weight**: _____ kg/lbs   Hours Slept: _____ hrs

Sport: _____   Workout: _____

Course: _____   Duration: _____   Distance: _____

Intensity: ☐ **Maximum**   ☐ **Hard**   ☐ **Medium**   ☐ **Minimum**

Average HR: _____ bpm   Target HR: _____ bpm

Feeling: ☐ **Fantastic**   ☐ **Good**   ☐ **Difficult**   ☐ **Very Difficult**

Weather   Temperature: _____ ° ___   Workout Gear: _____

Notes: _____

_____

Weekly Summary

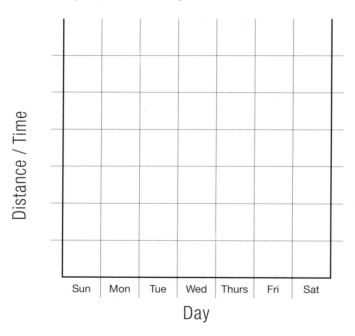

Total Time: _____   Total Distance: _____

Additional Information: _____

_____

_____

_____

_____

HAPPINESS LIES IN *good health* **and** *a bad memory.*
- Ingrid Bergman

Sunday

Vitals: **Resting HR**: _____ bpm   **Weight**: _____ kg/lbs   Hours Slept: _____ hrs

Sport: _____   Workout: _____

Course: _____   Duration: _____   Distance: _____

Intensity: ☐ **Maximum**   ☐ **Hard**   ☐ **Medium**   ☐ **Minimum**

Average HR: _____ bpm   Target HR: _____ bpm

Feeling: ☐ **Fantastic**   ☐ **Good**   ☐ **Difficult**   ☐ **Very Difficult**

Weather   Temperature: _____ ° ___   Workout Gear: _____

Notes:

Monday

Vitals: **Resting HR**: _____ bpm   **Weight**: _____ kg/lbs   Hours Slept: _____ hrs

Sport: _____   Workout: _____

Course: _____   Duration: _____   Distance: _____

Intensity: ☐ **Maximum**   ☐ **Hard**   ☐ **Medium**   ☐ **Minimum**

Average HR: _____ bpm   Target HR: _____ bpm

Feeling: ☐ **Fantastic**   ☐ **Good**   ☐ **Difficult**   ☐ **Very Difficult**

Weather   Temperature: _____ ° ___   Workout Gear: _____

Notes:

Tuesday

Vitals: **Resting HR**: _____ bpm   **Weight**: _____ kg/lbs   Hours Slept: _____ hrs

Sport: _____   Workout: _____

Course: _____   Duration: _____   Distance: _____

Intensity: ☐ **Maximum**   ☐ **Hard**   ☐ **Medium**   ☐ **Minimum**

Average HR: _____ bpm   Target HR: _____ bpm

Feeling: ☐ **Fantastic**   ☐ **Good**   ☐ **Difficult**   ☐ **Very Difficult**

Weather   Temperature: _____ ° ___   Workout Gear: _____

Notes:

Wednesday

Vitals: **Resting HR**: _____ bpm   **Weight**: _____ kg/lbs   Hours Slept: _____ hrs

Sport: _____   Workout: _____

Course: _____   Duration: _____   Distance: _____

Intensity: ☐ **Maximum**   ☐ **Hard**   ☐ **Medium**   ☐ **Minimum**

Average HR: _____ bpm   Target HR: _____ bpm

Feeling: ☐ **Fantastic**   ☐ **Good**   ☐ **Difficult**   ☐ **Very Difficult**

Weather   Temperature: _____ ° ___   Workout Gear: _____

Notes:

Thursday

Vitals: **Resting HR**: _____ bpm   **Weight**: _____ kg/lbs   Hours Slept: _____ hrs

Sport: _____   Workout: _____

Course: _____   Duration: _____   Distance: _____

Intensity: ☐ **Maximum**   ☐ **Hard**   ☐ **Medium**   ☐ **Minimum**

Average HR: _____ bpm   Target HR: _____ bpm

Feeling: ☐ **Fantastic**   ☐ **Good**   ☐ **Difficult**   ☐ **Very Difficult**

Weather   Temperature: _____ ° ___   Workout Gear: _____

Notes:

Friday

Vitals: **Resting HR**: _____ bpm   **Weight**: _____ kg/lbs   Hours Slept: _____ hrs

Sport: _____   Workout: _____

Course: _____   Duration: _____   Distance: _____

Intensity: ☐ **Maximum**   ☐ **Hard**   ☐ **Medium**   ☐ **Minimum**

Average HR: _____ bpm   Target HR: _____ bpm

Feeling: ☐ **Fantastic**   ☐ **Good**   ☐ **Difficult**   ☐ **Very Difficult**

Weather   Temperature: _____ ° ___   Workout Gear: _____

Notes:

Saturday

Date: _____   **Week 40**

Vitals: **Resting HR:** _____ bpm **Weight:** _____ kg/lbs Hours Slept: _____ hrs

Sport: _____ Workout: _____

Course: _____ Duration: _____ Distance: _____

Intensity: ☐ **Maximum** ☐ **Hard** ☐ **Medium** ☐ **Minimum**

Average HR: _____ bpm Target HR: _____ bpm

Feeling: ☐ **Fantastic** ☐ **Good** ☐ **Difficult** ☐ **Very Difficult**

Weather Temperature: _____ ° ___ Workout Gear: _____

Notes: _____

_____

_____

Weekly Summary

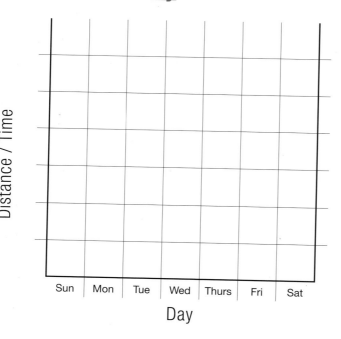

Total Time: _____ Total Distance: _____

Additional Information: _____

_____

_____

_____

_____

MOST PEOPLE RUN A RACE TO SEE WHO IS

fastest.

I RUN A RACE TO SEE WHO HAS THE MOST

guts.

- Steve Prefontaine

Sunday

Date: **Week 41**

Vitals: **Resting HR**: _____ bpm   **Weight**: _____ kg/lbs   Hours Slept: _____ hrs

Sport: _____   Workout: _____

Course: _____   Duration: _____   Distance: _____

Intensity: ☐ **Maximum**   ☐ **Hard**   ☐ **Medium**   ☐ **Minimum**

Average HR: _____ bpm   Target HR: _____ bpm

Feeling: ☐ **Fantastic**   ☐ **Good**   ☐ **Difficult**   ☐ **Very Difficult**

Weather   Temperature: _____ ° ___   Workout Gear: _____

Notes:

Monday

Date: **Week 41**

Vitals: **Resting HR**: _____ bpm   **Weight**: _____ kg/lbs   Hours Slept: _____ hrs

Sport: _____   Workout: _____

Course: _____   Duration: _____   Distance: _____

Intensity: ☐ **Maximum**   ☐ **Hard**   ☐ **Medium**   ☐ **Minimum**

Average HR: _____ bpm   Target HR: _____ bpm

Feeling: ☐ **Fantastic**   ☐ **Good**   ☐ **Difficult**   ☐ **Very Difficult**

Weather   Temperature: _____ ° ___   Workout Gear: _____

Notes:

Tuesday

Date: **Week 41**

Vitals: **Resting HR**: _____ bpm   **Weight**: _____ kg/lbs   Hours Slept: _____ hrs

Sport: _____   Workout: _____

Course: _____   Duration: _____   Distance: _____

Intensity: ☐ **Maximum**   ☐ **Hard**   ☐ **Medium**   ☐ **Minimum**

Average HR: _____ bpm   Target HR: _____ bpm

Feeling: ☐ **Fantastic**   ☐ **Good**   ☐ **Difficult**   ☐ **Very Difficult**

Weather   Temperature: _____ ° ___   Workout Gear: _____

Notes:

Wednesday

Date: _____   **Week 41**

Vitals: **Resting HR:** _____ bpm   **Weight:** _____ kg/lbs   Hours Slept: _____ hrs

Sport: _____   Workout: _____

Course: _____   Duration: _____   Distance: _____

Intensity: ☐ **Maximum**   ☐ **Hard**   ☐ **Medium**   ☐ **Minimum**

Average HR: _____ bpm   Target HR: _____ bpm

Feeling: ☐ **Fantastic**   ☐ **Good**   ☐ **Difficult**   ☐ **Very Difficult**

Weather   Temperature: _____ ° ___   Workout Gear: _____

Notes:

_____

_____

Thursday

Date: _____   **Week 41**

Vitals: **Resting HR:** _____ bpm   **Weight:** _____ kg/lbs   Hours Slept: _____ hrs

Sport: _____   Workout: _____

Course: _____   Duration: _____   Distance: _____

Intensity: ☐ **Maximum**   ☐ **Hard**   ☐ **Medium**   ☐ **Minimum**

Average HR: _____ bpm   Target HR: _____ bpm

Feeling: ☐ **Fantastic**   ☐ **Good**   ☐ **Difficult**   ☐ **Very Difficult**

Weather   Temperature: _____ ° ___   Workout Gear: _____

Notes:

_____

_____

Friday

Date: _____   **Week 41**

Vitals: **Resting HR:** _____ bpm   **Weight:** _____ kg/lbs   Hours Slept: _____ hrs

Sport: _____   Workout: _____

Course: _____   Duration: _____   Distance: _____

Intensity: ☐ **Maximum**   ☐ **Hard**   ☐ **Medium**   ☐ **Minimum**

Average HR: _____ bpm   Target HR: _____ bpm

Feeling: ☐ **Fantastic**   ☐ **Good**   ☐ **Difficult**   ☐ **Very Difficult**

Weather   Temperature: _____ ° ___   Workout Gear: _____

Notes:

_____

_____

Saturday

Vitals: **Resting HR**: _____ bpm   **Weight**: _____ kg/lbs   Hours Slept: _____ hrs

Sport: _____   Workout: _____

Course: _____   Duration: _____   Distance: _____

Intensity: ☐ **Maximum**   ☐ **Hard**   ☐ **Medium**   ☐ **Minimum**

Average HR: _____ bpm   Target HR: _____ bpm

Feeling: ☐ **Fantastic**   ☐ **Good**   ☐ **Difficult**   ☐ **Very Difficult**

Weather   Temperature: _____ ° ___   Workout Gear: _____

Notes:

_____

_____

Weekly Summary

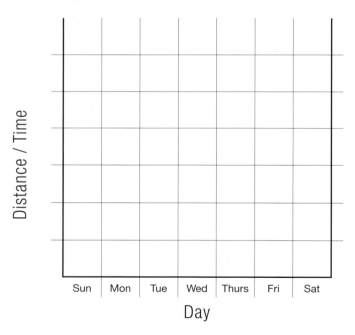

Total Time: _____   Total Distance: _____

Additional Information: _____

_____

_____

_____

Do *a little more* each day than you think you possibly can.

– Lowell Thomas

Sunday

Vitals: **Resting HR**: _____ bpm   **Weight**: _____ kg/lbs   Hours Slept: _____ hrs

Sport: _____   Workout: _____

Course: _____   Duration: _____   Distance: _____

Intensity: ☐ **Maximum**   ☐ **Hard**   ☐ **Medium**   ☐ **Minimum**

Average HR: _____ bpm   Target HR: _____ bpm

Feeling: ☐ **Fantastic**   ☐ **Good**   ☐ **Difficult**   ☐ **Very Difficult**

Weather   Temperature: _____ ° ___   Workout Gear: _____

Notes: _____

_____

_____

Monday

Date: _____   Week 42

Vitals: **Resting HR**: _____ bpm   **Weight**: _____ kg/lbs   Hours Slept: _____ hrs

Sport: _____   Workout: _____

Course: _____   Duration: _____   Distance: _____

Intensity: ☐ **Maximum**   ☐ **Hard**   ☐ **Medium**   ☐ **Minimum**

Average HR: _____ bpm   Target HR: _____ bpm

Feeling: ☐ **Fantastic**   ☐ **Good**   ☐ **Difficult**   ☐ **Very Difficult**

Weather   Temperature: _____ ° ___   Workout Gear: _____

Notes: _____

_____

_____

Tuesday

Date: _____   Week 42

Vitals: **Resting HR**: _____ bpm   **Weight**: _____ kg/lbs   Hours Slept: _____ hrs

Sport: _____   Workout: _____

Course: _____   Duration: _____   Distance: _____

Intensity: ☐ **Maximum**   ☐ **Hard**   ☐ **Medium**   ☐ **Minimum**

Average HR: _____ bpm   Target HR: _____ bpm

Feeling: ☐ **Fantastic**   ☐ **Good**   ☐ **Difficult**   ☐ **Very Difficult**

Weather   Temperature: _____ ° ___   Workout Gear: _____

Notes: _____

_____

_____

Wednesday

Date: _____   **Week 42**

Vitals: **Resting HR**: _____ bpm   **Weight**: _____ kg/lbs   Hours Slept: _____ hrs

Sport: _____   Workout: _____

Course: _____   Duration: _____   Distance: _____

Intensity: ☐ **Maximum**   ☐ **Hard**   ☐ **Medium**   ☐ **Minimum**

Average HR: _____ bpm   Target HR: _____ bpm

Feeling: ☐ **Fantastic**   ☐ **Good**   ☐ **Difficult**   ☐ **Very Difficult**

Weather   Temperature: _____ ° ___   Workout Gear: _____

Notes:

_____

_____

Thursday

Date: _____   **Week 42**

Vitals: **Resting HR**: _____ bpm   **Weight**: _____ kg/lbs   Hours Slept: _____ hrs

Sport: _____   Workout: _____

Course: _____   Duration: _____   Distance: _____

Intensity: ☐ **Maximum**   ☐ **Hard**   ☐ **Medium**   ☐ **Minimum**

Average HR: _____ bpm   Target HR: _____ bpm

Feeling: ☐ **Fantastic**   ☐ **Good**   ☐ **Difficult**   ☐ **Very Difficult**

Weather   Temperature: _____ ° ___   Workout Gear: _____

Notes:

_____

_____

Friday

Date: _____   **Week 42**

Vitals: **Resting HR**: _____ bpm   **Weight**: _____ kg/lbs   Hours Slept: _____ hrs

Sport: _____   Workout: _____

Course: _____   Duration: _____   Distance: _____

Intensity: ☐ **Maximum**   ☐ **Hard**   ☐ **Medium**   ☐ **Minimum**

Average HR: _____ bpm   Target HR: _____ bpm

Feeling: ☐ **Fantastic**   ☐ **Good**   ☐ **Difficult**   ☐ **Very Difficult**

Weather   Temperature: _____ ° ___   Workout Gear: _____

Notes:

_____

_____

Saturday

Vitals: **Resting HR**: _____ bpm   **Weight**: _____ kg/lbs   Hours Slept: _____ hrs

Sport: _____   Workout: _____

Course: _____   Duration: _____   Distance: _____

Intensity: □ **Maximum**   □ **Hard**   □ **Medium**   □ **Minimum**

Average HR: _____ bpm   Target HR: _____ bpm

Feeling: □ **Fantastic**   □ **Good**   □ **Difficult**   □ **Very Difficult**

Weather   Temperature: _____ ° ___   Workout Gear: _____

Notes: _____

_____

_____

Weekly Summary

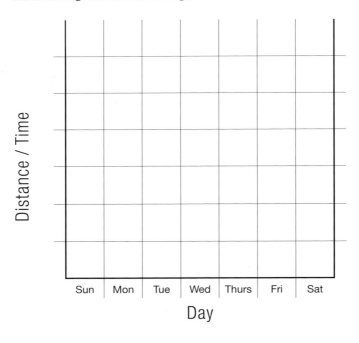

Total Time: _____   Total Distance: _____

Additional Information: _____

_____

_____

_____

_____

THE ONE THING

that I really appreciate about being a
runner is the incredible friendships and
camaraderie that we, as runners, share.

– JEN RHINES

Sunday

Vitals: **Resting HR**: _____ bpm   **Weight**: _____ kg/lbs   Hours Slept: _____ hrs

Sport: _____   Workout: _____

Course: _____   Duration: _____   Distance: _____

Intensity: □ **Maximum**   □ **Hard**   □ **Medium**   □ **Minimum**

Average HR: _____ bpm   Target HR: _____ bpm

Feeling: □ **Fantastic**   □ **Good**   □ **Difficult**   □ **Very Difficult**

Weather   Temperature: _____ ° ___   Workout Gear: _____

Notes: _____

_____

Monday

Date: _____   Week 43

Vitals: **Resting HR**: _____ bpm   **Weight**: _____ kg/lbs   Hours Slept: _____ hrs

Sport: _____   Workout: _____

Course: _____   Duration: _____   Distance: _____

Intensity: □ **Maximum**   □ **Hard**   □ **Medium**   □ **Minimum**

Average HR: _____ bpm   Target HR: _____ bpm

Feeling: □ **Fantastic**   □ **Good**   □ **Difficult**   □ **Very Difficult**

Weather   Temperature: _____ ° ___   Workout Gear: _____

Notes: _____

_____

Tuesday

Date: _____   Week 43

Vitals: **Resting HR**: _____ bpm   **Weight**: _____ kg/lbs   Hours Slept: _____ hrs

Sport: _____   Workout: _____

Course: _____   Duration: _____   Distance: _____

Intensity: □ **Maximum**   □ **Hard**   □ **Medium**   □ **Minimum**

Average HR: _____ bpm   Target HR: _____ bpm

Feeling: □ **Fantastic**   □ **Good**   □ **Difficult**   □ **Very Difficult**

Weather   Temperature: _____ ° ___   Workout Gear: _____

Notes: _____

_____

Wednesday

Date: _____   Week 43

Vitals: **Resting HR**: _____ bpm   **Weight**: _____ kg/lbs   Hours Slept: _____ hrs

Sport: _____   Workout: _____

Course: _____   Duration: _____   Distance: _____

Intensity: ☐ **Maximum**   ☐ **Hard**   ☐ **Medium**   ☐ **Minimum**

Average HR: _____ bpm   Target HR: _____ bpm

Feeling: ☐ **Fantastic**   ☐ **Good**   ☐ **Difficult**   ☐ **Very Difficult**

Weather   Temperature: _____ ° ___   Workout Gear: _____

Notes: _____

_____

Thursday

Date: _____   Week 43

Vitals: **Resting HR**: _____ bpm   **Weight**: _____ kg/lbs   Hours Slept: _____ hrs

Sport: _____   Workout: _____

Course: _____   Duration: _____   Distance: _____

Intensity: ☐ **Maximum**   ☐ **Hard**   ☐ **Medium**   ☐ **Minimum**

Average HR: _____ bpm   Target HR: _____ bpm

Feeling: ☐ **Fantastic**   ☐ **Good**   ☐ **Difficult**   ☐ **Very Difficult**

Weather   Temperature: _____ ° ___   Workout Gear: _____

Notes: _____

_____

Friday

Date: _____   Week 43

Vitals: **Resting HR**: _____ bpm   **Weight**: _____ kg/lbs   Hours Slept: _____ hrs

Sport: _____   Workout: _____

Course: _____   Duration: _____   Distance: _____

Intensity: ☐ **Maximum**   ☐ **Hard**   ☐ **Medium**   ☐ **Minimum**

Average HR: _____ bpm   Target HR: _____ bpm

Feeling: ☐ **Fantastic**   ☐ **Good**   ☐ **Difficult**   ☐ **Very Difficult**

Weather   Temperature: _____ ° ___   Workout Gear: _____

Notes: _____

_____

Saturday

Date: _____ **Week 43**

Vitals: **Resting HR:** _____ bpm   **Weight:** _____ kg/lbs   Hours Slept: _____ hrs

Sport: _____   Workout: _____

Course: _____   Duration: _____   Distance: _____

Intensity: ☐ **Maximum**   ☐ **Hard**   ☐ **Medium**   ☐ **Minimum**

Average HR: _____ bpm   Target HR: _____ bpm

Feeling: ☐ **Fantastic**   ☐ **Good**   ☐ **Difficult**   ☐ **Very Difficult**

Weather   Temperature: _____ ° ___   Workout Gear: _____

Notes: _____

_____

Weekly Summary

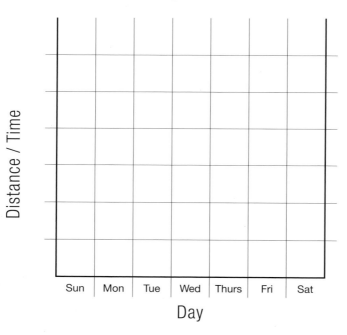

Total Time: _____   Total Distance: _____

Additional Information:

_____

_____

_____

_____

THERE IS NO
GREATER GLORY
FOR A MAN AS LONG AS HE LIVES
THAN THAT WHICH HE WINS
BY HIS OWN HANDS AND FEET.

– HOMER

Sunday

Vitals: **Resting HR**: _____ bpm   **Weight**: _____ kg/lbs   Hours Slept: _____ hrs

Sport: _____   Workout: _____

Course: _____   Duration: _____   Distance: _____

Intensity: ☐ **Maximum**   ☐ **Hard**   ☐ **Medium**   ☐ **Minimum**

Average HR: _____ bpm   Target HR: _____ bpm

Feeling: ☐ **Fantastic**   ☐ **Good**   ☐ **Difficult**   ☐ **Very Difficult**

Weather   Temperature: _____ ° ___   Workout Gear: _____

Notes: _____

_____

Monday

Vitals: **Resting HR**: _____ bpm   **Weight**: _____ kg/lbs   Hours Slept: _____ hrs

Sport: _____   Workout: _____

Course: _____   Duration: _____   Distance: _____

Intensity: ☐ **Maximum**   ☐ **Hard**   ☐ **Medium**   ☐ **Minimum**

Average HR: _____ bpm   Target HR: _____ bpm

Feeling: ☐ **Fantastic**   ☐ **Good**   ☐ **Difficult**   ☐ **Very Difficult**

Weather   Temperature: _____ ° ___   Workout Gear: _____

Notes: _____

_____

Tuesday

Vitals: **Resting HR**: _____ bpm   **Weight**: _____ kg/lbs   Hours Slept: _____ hrs

Sport: _____   Workout: _____

Course: _____   Duration: _____   Distance: _____

Intensity: ☐ **Maximum**   ☐ **Hard**   ☐ **Medium**   ☐ **Minimum**

Average HR: _____ bpm   Target HR: _____ bpm

Feeling: ☐ **Fantastic**   ☐ **Good**   ☐ **Difficult**   ☐ **Very Difficult**

Weather   Temperature: _____ ° ___   Workout Gear: _____

Notes: _____

_____

Wednesday

Vitals: **Resting HR:** _____ bpm   **Weight:** _____ kg/lbs   Hours Slept: _____ hrs

Sport: _____   Workout: _____

Course: _____   Duration: _____   Distance: _____

Intensity: ☐ **Maximum**   ☐ **Hard**   ☐ **Medium**   ☐ **Minimum**

Average HR: _____ bpm   Target HR: _____ bpm

Feeling: ☐ **Fantastic**   ☐ **Good**   ☐ **Difficult**   ☐ **Very Difficult**

Weather   Temperature: _____ ° ___   Workout Gear: _____

Notes: _____

Thursday

Vitals: **Resting HR:** _____ bpm   **Weight:** _____ kg/lbs   Hours Slept: _____ hrs

Sport: _____   Workout: _____

Course: _____   Duration: _____   Distance: _____

Intensity: ☐ **Maximum**   ☐ **Hard**   ☐ **Medium**   ☐ **Minimum**

Average HR: _____ bpm   Target HR: _____ bpm

Feeling: ☐ **Fantastic**   ☐ **Good**   ☐ **Difficult**   ☐ **Very Difficult**

Weather   Temperature: _____ ° ___   Workout Gear: _____

Notes: _____

Friday

Vitals: **Resting HR:** _____ bpm   **Weight:** _____ kg/lbs   Hours Slept: _____ hrs

Sport: _____   Workout: _____

Course: _____   Duration: _____   Distance: _____

Intensity: ☐ **Maximum**   ☐ **Hard**   ☐ **Medium**   ☐ **Minimum**

Average HR: _____ bpm   Target HR: _____ bpm

Feeling: ☐ **Fantastic**   ☐ **Good**   ☐ **Difficult**   ☐ **Very Difficult**

Weather   Temperature: _____ ° ___   Workout Gear: _____

Notes: _____

Saturday

Date: _____ **Week 44**

Vitals: **Resting HR:** _____ bpm **Weight:** _____ kg/lbs Hours Slept: _____ hrs

Sport: _____ Workout: _____

Course: _____ Duration: _____ Distance: _____

Intensity: ☐ **Maximum** ☐ **Hard** ☐ **Medium** ☐ **Minimum**

Average HR: _____ bpm Target HR: _____ bpm

Feeling: ☐ **Fantastic** ☐ **Good** ☐ **Difficult** ☐ **Very Difficult**

Weather Temperature: _____ ° ___ Workout Gear: _____

Notes: _____

_____

Weekly Summary

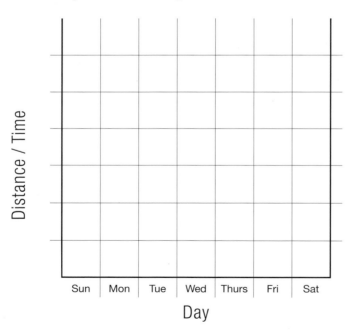

Total Time: _____ Total Distance: _____

Additional Information: _____

_____

_____

_____

There is no failure except in no longer trying.

- Elbert Hubbard

Sunday

Date: _____   **Week 45**

Vitals: **Resting HR**: _____ bpm   **Weight**: _____ kg/lbs   Hours Slept: _____ hrs

Sport: _____   Workout: _____

Course: _____   Duration: _____   Distance: _____

Intensity: ☐ **Maximum**   ☐ **Hard**   ☐ **Medium**   ☐ **Minimum**

Average HR: _____ bpm   Target HR: _____ bpm

Feeling: ☐ **Fantastic**   ☐ **Good**   ☐ **Difficult**   ☐ **Very Difficult**

Weather   Temperature: _____ ° ___   Workout Gear: _____

Notes: _____

_____

Monday

Date: _____   **Week 45**

Vitals: **Resting HR**: _____ bpm   **Weight**: _____ kg/lbs   Hours Slept: _____ hrs

Sport: _____   Workout: _____

Course: _____   Duration: _____   Distance: _____

Intensity: ☐ **Maximum**   ☐ **Hard**   ☐ **Medium**   ☐ **Minimum**

Average HR: _____ bpm   Target HR: _____ bpm

Feeling: ☐ **Fantastic**   ☐ **Good**   ☐ **Difficult**   ☐ **Very Difficult**

Weather   Temperature: _____ ° ___   Workout Gear: _____

Notes: _____

_____

Tuesday

Date: _____   **Week 45**

Vitals: **Resting HR**: _____ bpm   **Weight**: _____ kg/lbs   Hours Slept: _____ hrs

Sport: _____   Workout: _____

Course: _____   Duration: _____   Distance: _____

Intensity: ☐ **Maximum**   ☐ **Hard**   ☐ **Medium**   ☐ **Minimum**

Average HR: _____ bpm   Target HR: _____ bpm

Feeling: ☐ **Fantastic**   ☐ **Good**   ☐ **Difficult**   ☐ **Very Difficult**

Weather   Temperature: _____ ° ___   Workout Gear: _____

Notes: _____

_____

Wednesday

Vitals: **Resting HR**: _____ bpm   **Weight**: _____ kg/lbs   Hours Slept: _____ hrs

Sport: _____   Workout: _____

Course: _____   Duration: _____   Distance: _____

Intensity: ☐ **Maximum**   ☐ **Hard**   ☐ **Medium**   ☐ **Minimum**

Average HR: _____ bpm   Target HR: _____ bpm

Feeling: ☐ **Fantastic**   ☐ **Good**   ☐ **Difficult**   ☐ **Very Difficult**

Weather   Temperature: _____ ° ___   Workout Gear: _____

Notes: _____

_____

Thursday

Vitals: **Resting HR**: _____ bpm   **Weight**: _____ kg/lbs   Hours Slept: _____ hrs

Sport: _____   Workout: _____

Course: _____   Duration: _____   Distance: _____

Intensity: ☐ **Maximum**   ☐ **Hard**   ☐ **Medium**   ☐ **Minimum**

Average HR: _____ bpm   Target HR: _____ bpm

Feeling: ☐ **Fantastic**   ☐ **Good**   ☐ **Difficult**   ☐ **Very Difficult**

Weather   Temperature: _____ ° ___   Workout Gear: _____

Notes: _____

_____

Friday

Vitals: **Resting HR**: _____ bpm   **Weight**: _____ kg/lbs   Hours Slept: _____ hrs

Sport: _____   Workout: _____

Course: _____   Duration: _____   Distance: _____

Intensity: ☐ **Maximum**   ☐ **Hard**   ☐ **Medium**   ☐ **Minimum**

Average HR: _____ bpm   Target HR: _____ bpm

Feeling: ☐ **Fantastic**   ☐ **Good**   ☐ **Difficult**   ☐ **Very Difficult**

Weather   Temperature: _____ ° ___   Workout Gear: _____

Notes: _____

_____

Saturday

Vitals: **Resting HR:** _____ bpm   **Weight:** _____ kg/lbs   Hours Slept: _____ hrs

Sport: _____   Workout: _____

Course: _____   Duration: _____   Distance: _____

Intensity: ☐ **Maximum**   ☐ **Hard**   ☐ **Medium**   ☐ **Minimum**

Average HR: _____ bpm   Target HR: _____ bpm

Feeling: ☐ **Fantastic**   ☐ **Good**   ☐ **Difficult**   ☐ **Very Difficult**

Weather   Temperature: _____ ° ___   Workout Gear: _____

Notes: _____

_____

_____

Weekly Summary

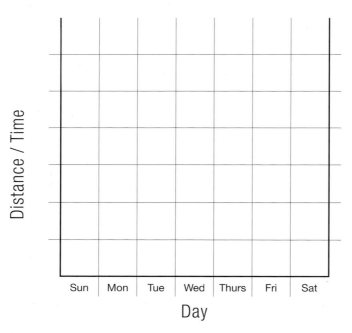

Total Time: _____   Total Distance: _____

Additional Information: _____

_____

_____

_____

Every runner

WAS ONCE A STRUGGLING BEGINNER.

– JOHN STANTON

Sunday

Date: _____   **Week 46**

Vitals: **Resting HR:** _____ bpm   **Weight:** _____ kg/lbs   Hours Slept: _____ hrs

Sport: _____   Workout: _____

Course: _____   Duration: _____   Distance: _____

Intensity: ☐ **Maximum**   ☐ **Hard**   ☐ **Medium**   ☐ **Minimum**

Average HR: _____ bpm   Target HR: _____ bpm

Feeling: ☐ **Fantastic**   ☐ **Good**   ☐ **Difficult**   ☐ **Very Difficult**

Weather   Temperature: _____ ° ___   Workout Gear: _____

Notes: _____

_____

_____

Monday

Date: _____   **Week 46**

Vitals: **Resting HR:** _____ bpm   **Weight:** _____ kg/lbs   Hours Slept: _____ hrs

Sport: _____   Workout: _____

Course: _____   Duration: _____   Distance: _____

Intensity: ☐ **Maximum**   ☐ **Hard**   ☐ **Medium**   ☐ **Minimum**

Average HR: _____ bpm   Target HR: _____ bpm

Feeling: ☐ **Fantastic**   ☐ **Good**   ☐ **Difficult**   ☐ **Very Difficult**

Weather   Temperature: _____ ° ___   Workout Gear: _____

Notes: _____

_____

_____

Tuesday

Date: _____   **Week 46**

Vitals: **Resting HR:** _____ bpm   **Weight:** _____ kg/lbs   Hours Slept: _____ hrs

Sport: _____   Workout: _____

Course: _____   Duration: _____   Distance: _____

Intensity: ☐ **Maximum**   ☐ **Hard**   ☐ **Medium**   ☐ **Minimum**

Average HR: _____ bpm   Target HR: _____ bpm

Feeling: ☐ **Fantastic**   ☐ **Good**   ☐ **Difficult**   ☐ **Very Difficult**

Weather   Temperature: _____ ° ___   Workout Gear: _____

Notes: _____

_____

_____

Wednesday

Vitals: **Resting HR:** _____ bpm   **Weight:** _____ kg/lbs   Hours Slept: _____ hrs

Sport: _____   Workout: _____

Course: _____   Duration: _____   Distance: _____

Intensity: ☐ **Maximum**   ☐ **Hard**   ☐ **Medium**   ☐ **Minimum**

Average HR: _____ bpm   Target HR: _____ bpm

Feeling: ☐ **Fantastic**   ☐ **Good**   ☐ **Difficult**   ☐ **Very Difficult**

Weather   Temperature: _____ ° ___   Workout Gear: _____

Notes:

Thursday

Vitals: **Resting HR:** _____ bpm   **Weight:** _____ kg/lbs   Hours Slept: _____ hrs

Sport: _____   Workout: _____

Course: _____   Duration: _____   Distance: _____

Intensity: ☐ **Maximum**   ☐ **Hard**   ☐ **Medium**   ☐ **Minimum**

Average HR: _____ bpm   Target HR: _____ bpm

Feeling: ☐ **Fantastic**   ☐ **Good**   ☐ **Difficult**   ☐ **Very Difficult**

Weather   Temperature: _____ ° ___   Workout Gear: _____

Notes:

Friday

Vitals: **Resting HR:** _____ bpm   **Weight:** _____ kg/lbs   Hours Slept: _____ hrs

Sport: _____   Workout: _____

Course: _____   Duration: _____   Distance: _____

Intensity: ☐ **Maximum**   ☐ **Hard**   ☐ **Medium**   ☐ **Minimum**

Average HR: _____ bpm   Target HR: _____ bpm

Feeling: ☐ **Fantastic**   ☐ **Good**   ☐ **Difficult**   ☐ **Very Difficult**

Weather   Temperature: _____ ° ___   Workout Gear: _____

Notes:

Saturday

Date: _____   **Week 46**

Vitals: **Resting HR**: _____ bpm   **Weight**: _____ kg/lbs   Hours Slept: _____ hrs

Sport: _____   Workout: _____

Course: _____   Duration: _____   Distance: _____

Intensity: ☐ **Maximum**   ☐ **Hard**   ☐ **Medium**   ☐ **Minimum**

Average HR: _____ bpm   Target HR: _____ bpm

Feeling: ☐ **Fantastic**   ☐ **Good**   ☐ **Difficult**   ☐ **Very Difficult**

Weather   Temperature: _____ ° ___   Workout Gear: _____

Notes: _____

_____

Weekly Summary

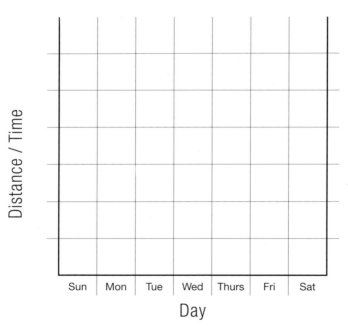

Total Time: _____   Total Distance: _____

Additional Information: _____

_____

_____

_____

I've always loved running...

You could go in any direction, fast or slow as you wanted, fighting the wind if you felt like it, seeking out new sights just on the strength of your feet and the courage of your lungs.

- Jesse Owens

Sunday

Date: _____   **Week 47**

Vitals: **Resting HR:** _____ bpm   **Weight:** _____ kg/lbs   Hours Slept: _____ hrs

Sport: _____   Workout: _____

Course: _____   Duration: _____   Distance: _____

Intensity: ☐ **Maximum**   ☐ **Hard**   ☐ **Medium**   ☐ **Minimum**

Average HR: _____ bpm   Target HR: _____ bpm

Feeling: ☐ **Fantastic**   ☐ **Good**   ☐ **Difficult**   ☐ **Very Difficult**

Weather   Temperature: _____ ° ___   Workout Gear: _____

Notes: _____

_____

_____

Monday

Date: _____   **Week 47**

Vitals: **Resting HR:** _____ bpm   **Weight:** _____ kg/lbs   Hours Slept: _____ hrs

Sport: _____   Workout: _____

Course: _____   Duration: _____   Distance: _____

Intensity: ☐ **Maximum**   ☐ **Hard**   ☐ **Medium**   ☐ **Minimum**

Average HR: _____ bpm   Target HR: _____ bpm

Feeling: ☐ **Fantastic**   ☐ **Good**   ☐ **Difficult**   ☐ **Very Difficult**

Weather   Temperature: _____ ° ___   Workout Gear: _____

Notes: _____

_____

_____

Tuesday

Date: _____   **Week 47**

Vitals: **Resting HR:** _____ bpm   **Weight:** _____ kg/lbs   Hours Slept: _____ hrs

Sport: _____   Workout: _____

Course: _____   Duration: _____   Distance: _____

Intensity: ☐ **Maximum**   ☐ **Hard**   ☐ **Medium**   ☐ **Minimum**

Average HR: _____ bpm   Target HR: _____ bpm

Feeling: ☐ **Fantastic**   ☐ **Good**   ☐ **Difficult**   ☐ **Very Difficult**

Weather   Temperature: _____ ° ___   Workout Gear: _____

Notes: _____

_____

_____

Wednesday

Date: _____   **Week 47**

Vitals: **Resting HR:** _____ bpm   **Weight:** _____ kg/lbs   Hours Slept: _____ hrs

Sport: _____   Workout: _____

Course: _____   Duration: _____   Distance: _____

Intensity: ☐ **Maximum**   ☐ **Hard**   ☐ **Medium**   ☐ **Minimum**

Average HR: _____ bpm   Target HR: _____ bpm

Feeling: ☐ **Fantastic**   ☐ **Good**   ☐ **Difficult**   ☐ **Very Difficult**

Weather   Temperature: _____ ° ___   Workout Gear: _____

Notes:

Thursday

Date: _____   **Week 47**

Vitals: **Resting HR:** _____ bpm   **Weight:** _____ kg/lbs   Hours Slept: _____ hrs

Sport: _____   Workout: _____

Course: _____   Duration: _____   Distance: _____

Intensity: ☐ **Maximum**   ☐ **Hard**   ☐ **Medium**   ☐ **Minimum**

Average HR: _____ bpm   Target HR: _____ bpm

Feeling: ☐ **Fantastic**   ☐ **Good**   ☐ **Difficult**   ☐ **Very Difficult**

Weather   Temperature: _____ ° ___   Workout Gear: _____

Notes:

Friday

Date: _____   **Week 47**

Vitals: **Resting HR:** _____ bpm   **Weight:** _____ kg/lbs   Hours Slept: _____ hrs

Sport: _____   Workout: _____

Course: _____   Duration: _____   Distance: _____

Intensity: ☐ **Maximum**   ☐ **Hard**   ☐ **Medium**   ☐ **Minimum**

Average HR: _____ bpm   Target HR: _____ bpm

Feeling: ☐ **Fantastic**   ☐ **Good**   ☐ **Difficult**   ☐ **Very Difficult**

Weather   Temperature: _____ ° ___   Workout Gear: _____

Notes:

Saturday

Vitals: **Resting HR**: _____ bpm   **Weight**: _____ kg/lbs   Hours Slept: _____ hrs

Sport: _____   Workout: _____

Course: _____   Duration: _____   Distance: _____

Intensity: ☐ **Maximum**   ☐ **Hard**   ☐ **Medium**   ☐ **Minimum**

Average HR: _____ bpm   Target HR: _____ bpm

Feeling: ☐ **Fantastic**   ☐ **Good**   ☐ **Difficult**   ☐ **Very Difficult**

Weather   Temperature: _____ ° __   Workout Gear: _____

Notes:

_____

_____

Weekly Summary

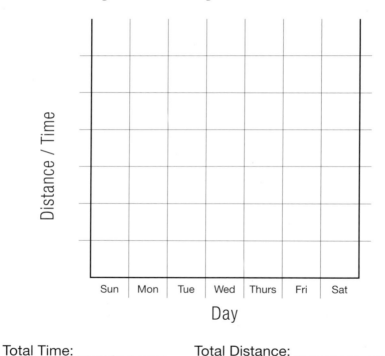

Total Time: _____   Total Distance: _____

Additional Information:

_____

_____

_____

_____

MOST RUNNERS RUN NOT BECAUSE
THEY WANT TO LIVE LONGER, BUT
BECAUSE THEY WANT TO
live life to the fullest.

– HARUKI MURAKAMI

Sunday

Date: _____ Week 48

Vitals: **Resting HR:** _____ bpm **Weight:** _____ kg/lbs Hours Slept: _____ hrs

Sport: _____ Workout: _____

Course: _____ Duration: _____ Distance: _____

Intensity: ☐ **Maximum** ☐ **Hard** ☐ **Medium** ☐ **Minimum**

Average HR: _____ bpm Target HR: _____ bpm

Feeling: ☐ **Fantastic** ☐ **Good** ☐ **Difficult** ☐ **Very Difficult**

Weather Temperature: _____ ° ___ Workout Gear: _____

Notes: _____

_____

_____

Monday

Date: _____ Week 48

Vitals: **Resting HR:** _____ bpm **Weight:** _____ kg/lbs Hours Slept: _____ hrs

Sport: _____ Workout: _____

Course: _____ Duration: _____ Distance: _____

Intensity: ☐ **Maximum** ☐ **Hard** ☐ **Medium** ☐ **Minimum**

Average HR: _____ bpm Target HR: _____ bpm

Feeling: ☐ **Fantastic** ☐ **Good** ☐ **Difficult** ☐ **Very Difficult**

Weather Temperature: _____ ° ___ Workout Gear: _____

Notes: _____

_____

_____

Tuesday

Date: _____ Week 48

Vitals: **Resting HR:** _____ bpm **Weight:** _____ kg/lbs Hours Slept: _____ hrs

Sport: _____ Workout: _____

Course: _____ Duration: _____ Distance: _____

Intensity: ☐ **Maximum** ☐ **Hard** ☐ **Medium** ☐ **Minimum**

Average HR: _____ bpm Target HR: _____ bpm

Feeling: ☐ **Fantastic** ☐ **Good** ☐ **Difficult** ☐ **Very Difficult**

Weather Temperature: _____ ° ___ Workout Gear: _____

Notes: _____

_____

_____

Wednesday

Date: _____   **Week 48**

Vitals: **Resting HR**: _____ bpm   **Weight**: _____ kg/lbs   Hours Slept: _____ hrs

Sport: _____   Workout: _____

Course: _____   Duration: _____   Distance: _____

Intensity: ☐ **Maximum**   ☐ **Hard**   ☐ **Medium**   ☐ **Minimum**

Average HR: _____ bpm   Target HR: _____ bpm

Feeling: ☐ **Fantastic**   ☐ **Good**   ☐ **Difficult**   ☐ **Very Difficult**

Weather   Temperature: _____ ° ___   Workout Gear: _____

Notes:

_____

_____

Thursday

Date: _____   **Week 48**

Vitals: **Resting HR**: _____ bpm   **Weight**: _____ kg/lbs   Hours Slept: _____ hrs

Sport: _____   Workout: _____

Course: _____   Duration: _____   Distance: _____

Intensity: ☐ **Maximum**   ☐ **Hard**   ☐ **Medium**   ☐ **Minimum**

Average HR: _____ bpm   Target HR: _____ bpm

Feeling: ☐ **Fantastic**   ☐ **Good**   ☐ **Difficult**   ☐ **Very Difficult**

Weather   Temperature: _____ ° ___   Workout Gear: _____

Notes:

_____

_____

Friday

Date: _____   **Week 48**

Vitals: **Resting HR**: _____ bpm   **Weight**: _____ kg/lbs   Hours Slept: _____ hrs

Sport: _____   Workout: _____

Course: _____   Duration: _____   Distance: _____

Intensity: ☐ **Maximum**   ☐ **Hard**   ☐ **Medium**   ☐ **Minimum**

Average HR: _____ bpm   Target HR: _____ bpm

Feeling: ☐ **Fantastic**   ☐ **Good**   ☐ **Difficult**   ☐ **Very Difficult**

Weather   Temperature: _____ ° ___   Workout Gear: _____

Notes:

_____

_____

Saturday

Vitals: **Resting HR**: _____ bpm   **Weight**: _____ kg/lbs   Hours Slept: _____ hrs

Sport: _____   Workout: _____

Course: _____   Duration: _____   Distance: _____

Intensity: ☐ **Maximum**   ☐ **Hard**   ☐ **Medium**   ☐ **Minimum**

Average HR: _____ bpm   Target HR: _____ bpm

Feeling: ☐ **Fantastic**   ☐ **Good**   ☐ **Difficult**   ☐ **Very Difficult**

Weather   Temperature: _____ ° ___   Workout Gear: _____

Notes:

_____

_____

Weekly Summary

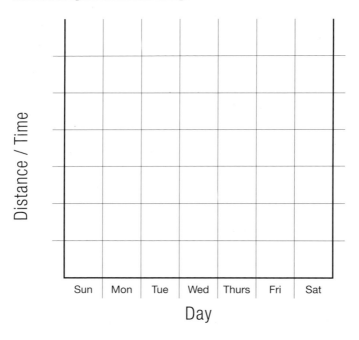

Total Time: _____   Total Distance: _____

Additional Information:

_____

_____

_____

_____

YOU WILL NEVER REGRET
THE RUN YOU DID...
BUT ALWAYS REGRET
THE RUN YOU MISSED.
– JOHN STANTON

Sunday

Date: _____ **Week 49**

Vitals: **Resting HR:** _____ bpm   **Weight:** _____ kg/lbs   Hours Slept: _____ hrs

Sport: _____   Workout: _____

Course: _____   Duration: _____   Distance: _____

Intensity: □ **Maximum**   □ **Hard**   □ **Medium**   □ **Minimum**

Average HR: _____ bpm   Target HR: _____ bpm

Feeling: □ **Fantastic**   □ **Good**   □ **Difficult**   □ **Very Difficult**

Weather   Temperature: _____ ° ___   Workout Gear: _____

Notes: _____

_____

Monday

Date: _____ **Week 49**

Vitals: **Resting HR:** _____ bpm   **Weight:** _____ kg/lbs   Hours Slept: _____ hrs

Sport: _____   Workout: _____

Course: _____   Duration: _____   Distance: _____

Intensity: □ **Maximum**   □ **Hard**   □ **Medium**   □ **Minimum**

Average HR: _____ bpm   Target HR: _____ bpm

Feeling: □ **Fantastic**   □ **Good**   □ **Difficult**   □ **Very Difficult**

Weather   Temperature: _____ ° ___   Workout Gear: _____

Notes: _____

_____

Tuesday

Date: _____ **Week 49**

Vitals: **Resting HR:** _____ bpm   **Weight:** _____ kg/lbs   Hours Slept: _____ hrs

Sport: _____   Workout: _____

Course: _____   Duration: _____   Distance: _____

Intensity: □ **Maximum**   □ **Hard**   □ **Medium**   □ **Minimum**

Average HR: _____ bpm   Target HR: _____ bpm

Feeling: □ **Fantastic**   □ **Good**   □ **Difficult**   □ **Very Difficult**

Weather   Temperature: _____ ° ___   Workout Gear: _____

Notes: _____

_____

Wednesday

Vitals: **Resting HR:** _____ bpm   **Weight:** _____ kg/lbs   Hours Slept: _____ hrs

Sport: _____   Workout: _____

Course: _____   Duration: _____   Distance: _____

Intensity: ☐ **Maximum**   ☐ **Hard**   ☐ **Medium**   ☐ **Minimum**

Average HR: _____ bpm   Target HR: _____ bpm

Feeling: ☐ **Fantastic**   ☐ **Good**   ☐ **Difficult**   ☐ **Very Difficult**

Weather   Temperature: _____ ° ___   Workout Gear: _____

Notes:

Thursday

Vitals: **Resting HR:** _____ bpm   **Weight:** _____ kg/lbs   Hours Slept: _____ hrs

Sport: _____   Workout: _____

Course: _____   Duration: _____   Distance: _____

Intensity: ☐ **Maximum**   ☐ **Hard**   ☐ **Medium**   ☐ **Minimum**

Average HR: _____ bpm   Target HR: _____ bpm

Feeling: ☐ **Fantastic**   ☐ **Good**   ☐ **Difficult**   ☐ **Very Difficult**

Weather   Temperature: _____ ° ___   Workout Gear: _____

Notes:

Friday

Vitals: **Resting HR:** _____ bpm   **Weight:** _____ kg/lbs   Hours Slept: _____ hrs

Sport: _____   Workout: _____

Course: _____   Duration: _____   Distance: _____

Intensity: ☐ **Maximum**   ☐ **Hard**   ☐ **Medium**   ☐ **Minimum**

Average HR: _____ bpm   Target HR: _____ bpm

Feeling: ☐ **Fantastic**   ☐ **Good**   ☐ **Difficult**   ☐ **Very Difficult**

Weather   Temperature: _____ ° ___   Workout Gear: _____

Notes:

Saturday

Date: _____   **Week 49**

Vitals: **Resting HR**: _____ bpm   **Weight**: _____ kg/lbs   Hours Slept: _____ hrs

Sport: _____   Workout: _____

Course: _____   Duration: _____   Distance: _____

Intensity: ☐ **Maximum**   ☐ **Hard**   ☐ **Medium**   ☐ **Minimum**

Average HR: _____ bpm   Target HR: _____ bpm

Feeling: ☐ **Fantastic**   ☐ **Good**   ☐ **Difficult**   ☐ **Very Difficult**

Weather   Temperature: _____ ° ___   Workout Gear: _____

Notes: _____

_____

Weekly Summary

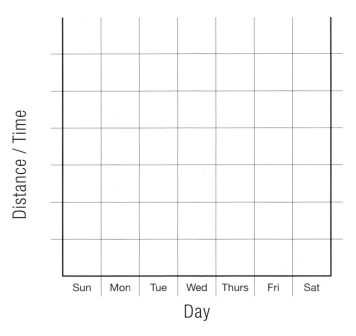

Total Time: _____   Total Distance: _____

Additional Information: _____

_____

_____

_____

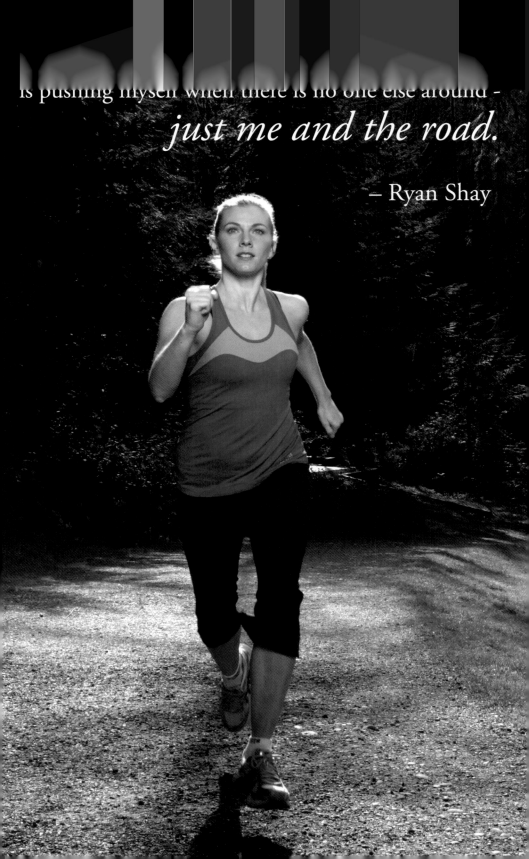

is pushing myself when there is no one else around –
just me and the road.

– Ryan Shay

Sunday

Date: _____   **Week 50**

Vitals: **Resting HR**: _____ bpm   **Weight**: _____ kg/lbs   Hours Slept: _____ hrs

Sport: _____   Workout: _____

Course: _____   Duration: _____   Distance: _____

Intensity: ☐ **Maximum**   ☐ **Hard**   ☐ **Medium**   ☐ **Minimum**

Average HR: _____ bpm   Target HR: _____ bpm

Feeling: ☐ **Fantastic**   ☐ **Good**   ☐ **Difficult**   ☐ **Very Difficult**

Weather   Temperature: _____ ° ___   Workout Gear: _____

Notes:

_____

_____

Monday

Date: _____   **Week 50**

Vitals: **Resting HR**: _____ bpm   **Weight**: _____ kg/lbs   Hours Slept: _____ hrs

Sport: _____   Workout: _____

Course: _____   Duration: _____   Distance: _____

Intensity: ☐ **Maximum**   ☐ **Hard**   ☐ **Medium**   ☐ **Minimum**

Average HR: _____ bpm   Target HR: _____ bpm

Feeling: ☐ **Fantastic**   ☐ **Good**   ☐ **Difficult**   ☐ **Very Difficult**

Weather   Temperature: _____ ° ___   Workout Gear: _____

Notes:

_____

_____

Tuesday

Date: _____   **Week 50**

Vitals: **Resting HR**: _____ bpm   **Weight**: _____ kg/lbs   Hours Slept: _____ hrs

Sport: _____   Workout: _____

Course: _____   Duration: _____   Distance: _____

Intensity: ☐ **Maximum**   ☐ **Hard**   ☐ **Medium**   ☐ **Minimum**

Average HR: _____ bpm   Target HR: _____ bpm

Feeling: ☐ **Fantastic**   ☐ **Good**   ☐ **Difficult**   ☐ **Very Difficult**

Weather   Temperature: _____ ° ___   Workout Gear: _____

Notes:

_____

_____

Wednesday

Date: _____   **Week 50**

Vitals: **Resting HR:** _____ bpm   **Weight:** _____ kg/lbs   Hours Slept: _____ hrs

Sport: _____   Workout: _____

Course: _____   Duration: _____   Distance: _____

Intensity: ☐ **Maximum**   ☐ **Hard**   ☐ **Medium**   ☐ **Minimum**

Average HR: _____ bpm   Target HR: _____ bpm

Feeling: ☐ **Fantastic**   ☐ **Good**   ☐ **Difficult**   ☐ **Very Difficult**

Weather   Temperature: _____ ° ___   Workout Gear: _____

Notes: _____

_____

_____

Thursday

Date: _____   **Week 50**

Vitals: **Resting HR:** _____ bpm   **Weight:** _____ kg/lbs   Hours Slept: _____ hrs

Sport: _____   Workout: _____

Course: _____   Duration: _____   Distance: _____

Intensity: ☐ **Maximum**   ☐ **Hard**   ☐ **Medium**   ☐ **Minimum**

Average HR: _____ bpm   Target HR: _____ bpm

Feeling: ☐ **Fantastic**   ☐ **Good**   ☐ **Difficult**   ☐ **Very Difficult**

Weather   Temperature: _____ ° ___   Workout Gear: _____

Notes: _____

_____

_____

Friday

Date: _____   **Week 50**

Vitals: **Resting HR:** _____ bpm   **Weight:** _____ kg/lbs   Hours Slept: _____ hrs

Sport: _____   Workout: _____

Course: _____   Duration: _____   Distance: _____

Intensity: ☐ **Maximum**   ☐ **Hard**   ☐ **Medium**   ☐ **Minimum**

Average HR: _____ bpm   Target HR: _____ bpm

Feeling: ☐ **Fantastic**   ☐ **Good**   ☐ **Difficult**   ☐ **Very Difficult**

Weather   Temperature: _____ ° ___   Workout Gear: _____

Notes: _____

_____

_____

Saturday

Vitals: **Resting HR:** _____ bpm   **Weight:** _____ kg/lbs   Hours Slept: _____ hrs

Sport: _____   Workout: _____

Course: _____   Duration: _____   Distance: _____

Intensity: ☐ **Maximum**   ☐ **Hard**   ☐ **Medium**   ☐ **Minimum**

Average HR: _____ bpm   Target HR: _____ bpm

Feeling: ☐ **Fantastic**   ☐ **Good**   ☐ **Difficult**   ☐ **Very Difficult**

Weather   Temperature: _____ ° ___   Workout Gear: _____

Notes: _____

_____

Weekly Summary

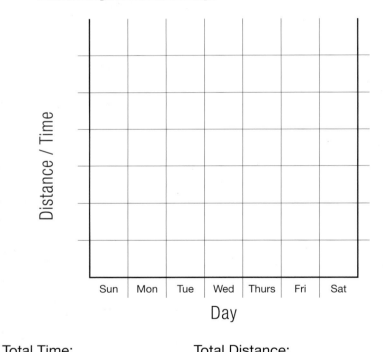

Total Time: _____   Total Distance: _____

Additional Information: _____

_____

_____

_____

_____

Luck has **nothing** to do with it.
- *Anonymous*

Sunday

Date: _____ **Week 51**

Vitals: **Resting HR:** _____ bpm   **Weight:** _____ kg/lbs   Hours Slept: _____ hrs

Sport: _____   Workout: _____

Course: _____   Duration: _____   Distance: _____

Intensity: ☐ **Maximum**   ☐ **Hard**   ☐ **Medium**   ☐ **Minimum**

Average HR: _____ bpm   Target HR: _____ bpm

Feeling: ☐ **Fantastic**   ☐ **Good**   ☐ **Difficult**   ☐ **Very Difficult**

Weather   Temperature: _____ ° ___   Workout Gear: _____

Notes:

Monday

Date: _____ **Week 51**

Vitals: **Resting HR:** _____ bpm   **Weight:** _____ kg/lbs   Hours Slept: _____ hrs

Sport: _____   Workout: _____

Course: _____   Duration: _____   Distance: _____

Intensity: ☐ **Maximum**   ☐ **Hard**   ☐ **Medium**   ☐ **Minimum**

Average HR: _____ bpm   Target HR: _____ bpm

Feeling: ☐ **Fantastic**   ☐ **Good**   ☐ **Difficult**   ☐ **Very Difficult**

Weather   Temperature: _____ ° ___   Workout Gear: _____

Notes:

Tuesday

Date: _____ **Week 51**

Vitals: **Resting HR:** _____ bpm   **Weight:** _____ kg/lbs   Hours Slept: _____ hrs

Sport: _____   Workout: _____

Course: _____   Duration: _____   Distance: _____

Intensity: ☐ **Maximum**   ☐ **Hard**   ☐ **Medium**   ☐ **Minimum**

Average HR: _____ bpm   Target HR: _____ bpm

Feeling: ☐ **Fantastic**   ☐ **Good**   ☐ **Difficult**   ☐ **Very Difficult**

Weather   Temperature: _____ ° ___   Workout Gear: _____

Notes:

Wednesday

Date: _____   Week 51

Vitals: **Resting HR:** _____ bpm   **Weight:** _____ kg/lbs   Hours Slept: _____ hrs

Sport: _____   Workout: _____

Course: _____   Duration: _____   Distance: _____

Intensity: ☐ **Maximum**   ☐ **Hard**   ☐ **Medium**   ☐ **Minimum**

Average HR: _____ bpm   Target HR: _____ bpm

Feeling: ☐ **Fantastic**   ☐ **Good**   ☐ **Difficult**   ☐ **Very Difficult**

Weather   Temperature: _____ ° ___   Workout Gear: _____

Notes: _____

_____

Thursday

Date: _____   Week 51

Vitals: **Resting HR:** _____ bpm   **Weight:** _____ kg/lbs   Hours Slept: _____ hrs

Sport: _____   Workout: _____

Course: _____   Duration: _____   Distance: _____

Intensity: ☐ **Maximum**   ☐ **Hard**   ☐ **Medium**   ☐ **Minimum**

Average HR: _____ bpm   Target HR: _____ bpm

Feeling: ☐ **Fantastic**   ☐ **Good**   ☐ **Difficult**   ☐ **Very Difficult**

Weather   Temperature: _____ ° ___   Workout Gear: _____

Notes: _____

_____

Friday

Date: _____   Week 51

Vitals: **Resting HR:** _____ bpm   **Weight:** _____ kg/lbs   Hours Slept: _____ hrs

Sport: _____   Workout: _____

Course: _____   Duration: _____   Distance: _____

Intensity: ☐ **Maximum**   ☐ **Hard**   ☐ **Medium**   ☐ **Minimum**

Average HR: _____ bpm   Target HR: _____ bpm

Feeling: ☐ **Fantastic**   ☐ **Good**   ☐ **Difficult**   ☐ **Very Difficult**

Weather   Temperature: _____ ° ___   Workout Gear: _____

Notes: _____

_____

Saturday

Date: _____   **Week 51**

Vitals: **Resting HR**: _____ bpm   **Weight**: _____ kg/lbs   Hours Slept: _____ hrs

Sport: _____   Workout: _____

Course: _____   Duration: _____   Distance: _____

Intensity: ☐ **Maximum**   ☐ **Hard**   ☐ **Medium**   ☐ **Minimum**

Average HR: _____ bpm   Target HR: _____ bpm

Feeling: ☐ **Fantastic**   ☐ **Good**   ☐ **Difficult**   ☐ **Very Difficult**

Weather   Temperature: _____ ° ___   Workout Gear: _____

Notes: _____

_____

Weekly Summary

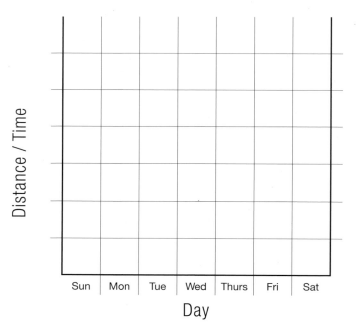

Total Time: _____   Total Distance: _____

Additional Information: _____

_____

_____

_____

_____

THE GREATEST **PLEASURE** IN LIFE IS DOING WHAT PEOPLE SAY YOU CANNOT DO.

- *Walter Bagehot*

Sunday

Date: _____   **Week 52**

Vitals: **Resting HR**: _____ bpm   **Weight**: _____ kg/lbs   Hours Slept: _____ hrs

Sport: _____   Workout: _____

Course: _____   Duration: _____   Distance: _____

Intensity: ☐ **Maximum**   ☐ **Hard**   ☐ **Medium**   ☐ **Minimum**

Average HR: _____ bpm   Target HR: _____ bpm

Feeling: ☐ **Fantastic**   ☐ **Good**   ☐ **Difficult**   ☐ **Very Difficult**

Weather   Temperature: _____ ° ___   Workout Gear: _____

Notes: _____

_____

_____

Monday

Date: _____   **Week 52**

Vitals: **Resting HR**: _____ bpm   **Weight**: _____ kg/lbs   Hours Slept: _____ hrs

Sport: _____   Workout: _____

Course: _____   Duration: _____   Distance: _____

Intensity: ☐ **Maximum**   ☐ **Hard**   ☐ **Medium**   ☐ **Minimum**

Average HR: _____ bpm   Target HR: _____ bpm

Feeling: ☐ **Fantastic**   ☐ **Good**   ☐ **Difficult**   ☐ **Very Difficult**

Weather   Temperature: _____ ° ___   Workout Gear: _____

Notes: _____

_____

_____

Tuesday

Date: _____   **Week 52**

Vitals: **Resting HR**: _____ bpm   **Weight**: _____ kg/lbs   Hours Slept: _____ hrs

Sport: _____   Workout: _____

Course: _____   Duration: _____   Distance: _____

Intensity: ☐ **Maximum**   ☐ **Hard**   ☐ **Medium**   ☐ **Minimum**

Average HR: _____ bpm   Target HR: _____ bpm

Feeling: ☐ **Fantastic**   ☐ **Good**   ☐ **Difficult**   ☐ **Very Difficult**

Weather   Temperature: _____ ° ___   Workout Gear: _____

Notes: _____

_____

_____

Wednesday

Date: _____ **Week 52**

Vitals: **Resting HR**: _____ bpm **Weight**: _____ kg/lbs Hours Slept: _____ hrs

Sport: _____ Workout: _____

Course: _____ Duration: _____ Distance: _____

Intensity: □ **Maximum** □ **Hard** □ **Medium** □ **Minimum**

Average HR: _____ bpm Target HR: _____ bpm

Feeling: □ **Fantastic** □ **Good** □ **Difficult** □ **Very Difficult**

Weather   Temperature: _____ ° __ Workout Gear: _____

Notes:

Thursday

Date: _____ **Week 52**

Vitals: **Resting HR**: _____ bpm **Weight**: _____ kg/lbs Hours Slept: _____ hrs

Sport: _____ Workout: _____

Course: _____ Duration: _____ Distance: _____

Intensity: □ **Maximum** □ **Hard** □ **Medium** □ **Minimum**

Average HR: _____ bpm Target HR: _____ bpm

Feeling: □ **Fantastic** □ **Good** □ **Difficult** □ **Very Difficult**

Weather   Temperature: _____ ° __ Workout Gear: _____

Notes:

Friday

Date: _____ **Week 52**

Vitals: **Resting HR**: _____ bpm **Weight**: _____ kg/lbs Hours Slept: _____ hrs

Sport: _____ Workout: _____

Course: _____ Duration: _____ Distance: _____

Intensity: □ **Maximum** □ **Hard** □ **Medium** □ **Minimum**

Average HR: _____ bpm Target HR: _____ bpm

Feeling: □ **Fantastic** □ **Good** □ **Difficult** □ **Very Difficult**

Weather   Temperature: _____ ° __ Workout Gear: _____

Notes:

Saturday

Date: _____ **Week 52**

Vitals: **Resting HR**: _____ bpm   **Weight**: _____ kg/lbs   Hours Slept: _____ hrs

Sport: _____   Workout: _____

Course: _____   Duration: _____   Distance: _____

Intensity: ☐ **Maximum**   ☐ **Hard**   ☐ **Medium**   ☐ **Minimum**

Average HR: _____ bpm   Target HR: _____ bpm

Feeling: ☐ **Fantastic**   ☐ **Good**   ☐ **Difficult**   ☐ **Very Difficult**

Weather   Temperature: _____ ° ___   Workout Gear: _____

Notes: _____

_____

Weekly Summary

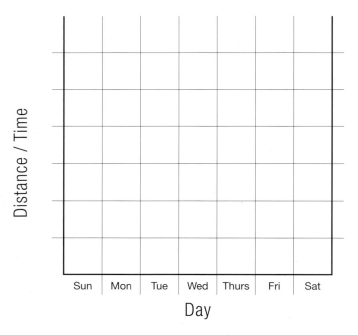

Total Time: _____   Total Distance: _____

Additional Information: _____

_____

_____

_____

254

A FINISHER'S MEDAL ISN'T FOR HOW FAST
OR HOW SLOW YOU ARE...IT'S AWARDED
BECAUSE YOU DIDN'T QUIT.

- JOHN STANTON

Race Records

Date	Name/Location	Distance	Time	Pace

Date	Name/Location	Distance	Time	Pace

Index